Your Daughter,
Your Advocate

A daughter's account of caring for her mother against Lewy body dementia in a flawed care system.

Bonnie Manns Roache

Copyright Page

The information included is based on the author's personal experience and opinions, perceptions, and explicit evidence.

Neither the author nor the publisher can be held responsible for the use of the information provided within this book. Please always consult a trained professional before making any decision regarding treatment of yourself or others.

For more information, email bmroache@gmail.com
ISBN: **978-0-578-26366-3**

Dedication

This book is dedicated to the memory of my mother, Mary Alice Jackson, who bravely fought the battle against Lewy body dementia.

This book is dedicated to those of you on your own journey against this unrelenting disease and trying your best to make the best decisions you can.

Table of Contents

Chapter 1

CAREGIVER PERSPECTIVES

The Caregiver

I looked around to make sure nothing was put away in a strange place. Ms. Mary was cleaning her home, apartment 409 of the senior building. The plate and coffee cup on the table of her living room-dining combo indicated she'd already eaten breakfast. I noted a biscuit with sausage or chicken, sliced cantaloupe, and coffee in the journal so Ms. Bonnie, her daughter, would know what she had eaten today. I stayed out of the way, allowing Ms. Mary to go about her cleaning.

I waited for her to settle down so I could give her morning meds and check her blood sugar. If I pushed her, it wouldn't be a good day. She was in her bedroom meddling around. Her bed was neatly made, and she had already showered and dressed. After the bedroom, she cleaned her kitchen. Ms. Mary cleaned her little one-bedroom apartment quite well. She didn't like people roaming around her house or through her things. She watched me if I moved from my chair and would let me know real quick if I moved the wrong way. Everything looked ok.

"You don't have to come here and sit with me. I don't need a babysitter," Ms. Mary said.

"Oh, no ma'am, I just came by to visit you and talk with you," I said quickly so I wouldn't be in trouble. Since she was talking to me, I chatted with her about Gramma Hazel, Aunt Emma, and Ms. Willie Mae an' 'nem. "Gramma Hazel told me to come over here and see you. My Gramma used to tell me about Cousin Lucille and her children."

Talking about those ol' folks from her past usually made her smile. I didn't know when she knew them, all I knew was Ms. Bonnie, her daughter, told me to use this strategy to make Ms. Mary feel comfortable with me. So, Ms. Mary and I talked and laughed about all those ol' folks as if I knew them too.

"Cousin Mary, you ready to take your medicine?"

"Whatever," she replied sarcastically. Ms. Mary stopped her cleaning and sat on the sofa in the living room. She extended her finger in cooperation. I checked her blood sugar and blood pressure as we did every day. She usually allowed me to take vitals as long as I didn't push her. I handed her a small plastic box labeled "Tues AM" that Ms. Bonnie had already set up with her morning meds. She opened it and poured three small pills into her hand, then put the pills in her mouth. I handed her a glass of water. She drank the water and handed it back. Then she got up from the sofa and went into the kitchen to get herself a cup of water. I stood in the kitchen doorway pretending to just chat with her while I watched to make sure she had swallowed the pills. I didn't dare tell her I had already given her a cup of water. I learned to let her do what she wanted as long as she was safe.

"Cousin Mary, you cleaned this kitchen real good!" Ms. Mary grinned.

"I always cleaned the house. My momma didn't play that." We mostly watched TV the rest of the day and laughed at the folks on *Judge Judy*. She always thought those people were quite funny. Today was a good day.

Bonnie

After work, I arrived at Mom's apartment in Clairemont. I usually went to give evening meds and make sure she ate dinner before I headed home twenty minutes away. I checked the indoor camera from my cell phone before arriving to confirm that she was ok inside. I had a key, but I knocked. Mom opened the door. "Hey, how are you doing?"

She seemed happy to see me. I entered the apartment. "I'm doing good, how are you doing today? Did Cousin Hazel's granddaughter come by today to see you?" I was referring to the caregiver that I knew had come earlier.

"Who? I haven't seen her." I wasn't sure if Mom didn't remember or if she was on to our charade and realized the woman wasn't related to her.

I had several tasks to do during my visits without making Mom aware that it was part of caring for her. I learned to look for things that weren't obviously misplaced. My routine was to open the fridge, cabinets, oven, microwave, look under the mattress and under and behind things. Then, I would check the calendar on the wall which listed the schedule for the caregivers—including Aunt Betty and myself—to be sure I had adequate caregiver coverage and hadn't double-booked. Next, I checked the medication to make sure all pillboxes were filled for the next few days. It was easier to monitor what she was taking that way.

We used to put pill bottles on the entry hall closet shelf. Mom was usually with caregivers going into that hallway closet, but if they went into her bedroom, she got very agitated. "You wouldn't want somebody going all over your house!" We couldn't argue with that, so we put journals, medication, or whatever the caregiver needed in that hallway closet. That worked for a while, then we realized she was going into the bottles, and we weren't sure if she was taking the pills when she was alone.

I had to come up with another solution for medication management. I put her pills in little plastic containers I found at Dollar Tree. I labeled them AM and PM for each day. The caregiver only had to retrieve the box labeled for that day, morning or evening, hand them to her, and confirm that she actually took them. Where could I leave them so Mom wouldn't find them? The safe in the closet held about ten little pillboxes and it had a key lock. That became our system. We always had to stay a plan ahead of Lewy.

Aunt Betty

I arrived at Clairemont to visit my sister, smiling and talking to everyone from the lobby up to the fourth floor. I visited Sista often so all the regulars recognized me, and I recognized them. I was scheduled to come by some afternoons after the morning caregiver left.

Sometimes, I came by early before the caregiver left, and the three of us would sit around and talk. I wanted to have a positive relationship with anyone caring for my sister. Sista enjoyed the chats with just the three of us because she could participate in the conversation. Some days my knees hurt, but I went to visit her anyway. I brought snacks and we watched TV together at her apartment. I had retired from the hospital, so I was familiar with the dementia behaviors. Regardless of the dementia, Sista was like a mother to me, and I would go wherever she needed me.

I knocked on the door at apartment 409. Bonnie had given me a key, but I usually knocked. She opened the door. "Hey, Mary Alice! I brought you some goodies!"

"Hey!" she replied. "Where you going?"

"I'm coming to hang out with you!" Based on the big cardboard box in front of the sofa, I assumed she was going through her box of CDs and cassettes again. The TV was on. I put a bag of snacks on the counter of the small kitchenette. "I brought you some oranges and some Cheese-Its."

"Thank you," she said. She was always very appreciative. We sat and watched the episode of *Bonanza* on TV. She liked Westerns and the English TV Show *Keeping Up Appearances*. When she lived with me, she and I used to sit up late at night watching that show.

She started getting restless, walking back and forth. The weather was clear and not too hot. I decided to get her outside of the apartment for some sunshine. She loved to eat out. "Sista, you want to go out to eat?"

"Ok. If you want to go." She always said that, but I knew it meant yes. I checked to make sure her clothes were on correctly, rather than inside out or backward. She was dressed decently. Sista always wanted to look right when she went out. She combed her hair and put on some face powder and lipstick. Those were still familiar routines to her. I helped her find her shoes and a sweater. Even before dementia, it always took her a while to get ready to go somewhere, so I knew it might be an hour. We finally left and got on the elevator to the lobby. As we walked through the lobby, Sista spoke to everybody we passed. She didn't know them, but she was polite and friendly with everyone. "You're looking mighty good today," she said. Sista saw those people as old folks and she had a caring heart for old people.

We went to the Golden Corral down the street before the lunch hour and senior discount were over. We had been to Golden Corral many times. The staff recognized us now. The young lady that usually served us came right to our table with a smile. We always sat in the same area. Sista made her regular trip around the buffet table. As the disease progressed, she was still comfortable and familiar with the buffet. She got her raisin salad, piece of fried chicken, and a little of this and that. Since she had been a cook, she would taste and critique the food. "This taste pretty good," or "I don't know who cooked these greens, ain't no seasoning in them!"

She always tipped the server. Sista had worked hard, and she appreciated other people who worked hard to make a living. She was always respectful to servers. Anything we couldn't eat on our plates, Sista rolled up in some napkins and put in her bag. We thought it was bad to waste food. Usually, it was just a few cookies or an occasional brownie. I'm sure the staff saw her, but they never said anything.

Chapter 2

CAUSES, SYMPTOMS, AND SIGNS

Traumatic Experiences

As I think about my mom's life and what may have contributed to her getting dementia, I reflect on traumatic events and early signs. Of course, I am no medical or scientific guru, so my theory is just a daughter's viewpoint based on what I believe.

First, one must understand Mom's childhood. I didn't think of it as traumatic until I listened to what she talked about when Lewy (a.k.a. Lewy body dementia) was in control. Mary Alice was the oldest of Lucille and John's six children: Johnnie Bell, Donnell, Earnest, Lue, and Betty. She was born in 1937 in Fort Gaines, GA, a small rural town in southwest Georgia where many blacks worked on farms, in cotton fields, and did domestic work as her parents did. Mary Alice often looked after the younger children when her parents were working. Lucille's sister, Mary Francis—a.k.a. Aunt Honey—helped with the children.

When Aunt Honey moved to Florida, Mary Alice took over looking after the other children when Lucille worked. She was the oldest and became the authority figure. They called her "Sista", and "You betta do what Sista says!" Her siblings respected what "Sista" said even as adults. During the Lewy episodes, her hallucinations often included "Where are the children? Where are those boys?" I suppose these were hallucinations of a time when she was young and was responsible for making sure the children were ok.

When I was five, Mom gave birth to a baby boy. I didn't understand what was happening, but I remember that night very well. Mom's husband made several trips between the hospital and the house to give my grandmother updates, and finally reported that the baby died. I didn't know how close I came to losing my mom that night. She had carried a full-term baby boy that never took a breath: Willie Frank Jackson. I never asked about the details of that delivery, but I heard the grown folks talking.

Mom came home in a wheelchair and couldn't walk. Doctors said she might never walk again. One day, my one-year-old cousin was bleeding after piercing his eye with a sharp object. She couldn't get to him. After that incident, Mom would pull herself from the chair by holding onto the wall to care for her nephew. I can still see her leaning against the wall, coming down the hallway with the toddler under one arm. I recall that scene many years later after Mom was in the Nursing Home and confined to a wheelchair again. She would lift herself from the wheelchair to a regular chair using her own weight. It reminded me of that day when I was five and watched her lean against the walls to walk again. Losing the baby and being confined to a wheelchair at age thirty-three must have been traumatic for Sista, someone who had taken care of five younger siblings.

Around 1995, I thought I was doing a great thing by facilitating my mother's early retirement due to disability. Months prior, I noticed she was dragging her right leg when she walked. I went to her next doctor's appointment with her and found out it was due to diabetic complications and the doctor had advised her to stay off her feet months prior. When I asked Mom why she hadn't mentioned it, she said, "I need to work because I need insurance."

She had worked as long as she could remember. Not working was never an option to her. With all good intentions, I started the process to apply for her disability and she retired at fifty-nine from the Marriott Marquis hotel. I didn't realize that would have a significant impact on her. In retrospect, I realized that she had relationships and a purpose through that job. She didn't drive, so she was home alone, connected primarily through phone conversations and occasional visits from her sister Betty. Her social outlet had been her job.

My next well-intentioned idea was that Mom should move back to our hometown to take care of her mother, Lucille, who had been the rock of the family. Grandma Lucille had aged over the years, and she lived alone in the family house. Mom was living alone in Atlanta. It made sense for them to be together. Mom moved back to Fort Gaines around 1999 to take care of her mother. Grandma loved having Sista there caring for her.

But after the move back home, Mom's behavioral changes became apparent. The family noticed Mom seemed angry, but no one addressed it because she was "Sista". That would be like talking back. Mom took care of Grandma Lucille until she passed in 2004. After that, Mom was alone again in the family house.

Research hasn't proven or disproven that the response to traumatic life events contributes to the onset of dementia, but it seemed to for Mom. She became a caregiver for her mother who was the epitome of survival to her when she was young. Mo, as she called her, was all she and her siblings had when they were growing up. Seeing her mother 24/7 revealed how frail her rock had become. I don't think Mom ever processed the reality of her own mother's decline and eventual transition. I know now, after my own experience caring for her, that being a caregiver 24/7 and losing your loved one each day can be traumatic if those feelings aren't dealt with. Isolation and grief create an ideal environment for depression and other health issues.

Early Signs

For ten years after my grandmother passed—2004 until 2014—before Mom was diagnosed, we had a continuous medical appointment routine. She remained in the family house in our hometown three hours south of Atlanta. As long as everything was fine, her diabetic, primary care, and other specialists in Atlanta rescheduled her next appointments every four to six months.

Two of her sisters, Johnnie and Lue, lived nearby. Although Mom was difficult, they visited or ran errands for her. She was still "Sista", and she had been their mother figure, their caregiver. But their attempts to help would provoke her anger. We noticed fixations, paranoia, and confusion. She bought food as if to feed a large family. She fussed about children messing up her clean house, though there were no children. She lived alone. Whenever she was away from the house, she was convinced someone had been in her house messing with her things when she was gone. She would start writing checks or birthday cards and not complete them. We tried to respond to whatever was wrong, but she was angry about anything we tried to do to help. These were early signs that many of us dismissed as cantankerous or cynical or "Sista's just getting older."

A Familiar Place

In early 2014, I brought Mom to Atlanta for our usual cycle of medical appointments. During one of those appointments, we visited Dr. Flowers, the endocrinologist she'd been seeing for several years. Usually, I would drop her off at the door and park the car. This time, I walked with her because his office had moved a few visits ago, and I wasn't sure if she would remember to go to the new location. I showed her how easy it was. Just get on the elevator, go up one floor, walk down the long hall.

Once she was checked in, I went to the cafeteria to get something to eat as I hadn't eaten anything that morning. I intended to get back to Dr. Flowers's office before she was called back. I grabbed some fruit and juice and ate quickly. When I made my way back to Dr. Flowers' office, I expected to see Mom in the waiting room. She wasn't there. I assumed they had taken her back already. I asked the receptionist if Ms. Jackson was in the back. She said, "Let me check. I think Ms. Jackson left already."

Francine, Mom's usual nurse, came up and said, "Hey, Ms. Jackson is done. She left already." Apparently, her visit had been completed much sooner than I anticipated.

"How long ago did she leave?"

Francine paused. "About ten minutes, maybe." Mom usually waited for me in the office if I wasn't there. I assumed she went to the restroom in the hallway. She had to be between the office and the elevator. I hoped. I checked the restroom. She wasn't there. I hurried down the hallway to check the other restroom at the opposite end. She was not there either. I walked the path between Dr. Flowers' office and the car, the route I had shown her.

Maybe she had gone back toward the car looking for me. There was no sign of her. I walked the route back to Dr. Flowers' office again. Maybe she had gone back there, or I would pass her in the hallway. At this time, there had been no talk of dementia, just the increased moodiness and anger. Nothing we considered alarming. So, this wasn't like her. I didn't know what to think.

She knows this building better than I do, I thought. Maybe she went to see her vascular doctor located in the other building.

I hurried across the courtyard to the other building in the medical complex and took the elevator up to the vascular doctor's suite. The front desk nurse, who knows my mom, said, "No, Ms. Jackson hasn't been here today."

I looked around the waiting room anyway. This made no sense. I hurried back toward Dr. Flowers' office again. She still wasn't there. The nurse was concerned that I still hadn't found her. The nurse said, "If she comes back, we'll call you."

About thirty to forty minutes had passed. I had checked everywhere, she had disappeared. What could have happened? My stomach was in knots but I needed to pull it together. I found the security desk and asked if there had been any reports of a lost person. There were none, and the security guard seemed unconcerned about doing anything further. Thoughts of contacting the police entered my mind. This had never happened before. As I walked back to the hallway between Dr. Flowers' office and the elevator she would have taken, I looked right. Then left.

Then, I saw her walking up the hallway toward me. She had no sense of urgency or confusion. "Mom! Where have you been? I've been looking everywhere for you!"

She didn't have an explanation and didn't say much except, "I don't know."

"Did you go downstairs to look for me? Did you go to the bathroom?" I kept asking for a logical explanation but she didn't have one and my insistence seemed to aggravate her.

"Bonnie, I *don't know*!" I stopped asking and we left.

Months later, after the dementia diagnosis, I recalled that day and realized it was probably a sign of early dementia. She was confused by the hallway she had taken many times and had wandered around looking for something familiar. She probably didn't know what or whom she was looking for. I imagine she was more afraid than I was that day.

Christmas Gifts

Christmas season, 2014, was approaching. Mom's seventy-eighth birthday was in December. I didn't want to take her back home to South Georgia so close to the holiday. Usually, I planned a weekend to drive down, pick her up, and bring her to Atlanta to spend the holidays with us. But she was still here from her October medical visits which had continued into more follow-up appointments.

Christmas was a big holiday for Mom because it meant family. She wanted to make sure everybody got something to open. Mom was sorting through some gifts for the men in the family. She always bought Christmas gifts and decided later who she would give them to.

"Come here. I want to show you something." She led me to her bedroom in Aunt Betty's house where she stayed when she was in Atlanta. She had five men's items laid out on the bed.

She identified who she should give each gift to and wanted my input. As she pointed to each, she said, "I can give John—her son—a sweater. I can give Dee Dee this sweatshirt. Steve…" She pointed to the socks. The other two pairs of socks would go to other relatives. That went on about twenty minutes as she kept reassigning the gifts over and over. She wasn't changing her mind. Mom didn't seem to realize the decision was already made or that we had gone through the exercise already. After that, I knew something was wrong with Momma.

Journaling

Doctor appointments were challenging to schedule, so I wanted the visits to be as effective as possible. I kept a journal of notes to share with her doctors. The notes described the bizarre behaviors, anger, and withdrawal we were seeing in Mom. I wrote it all down so they could read it before the visit. When I tried describing the behaviors to the doctor in Mom's presence, Mom became very agitated, thinking we were talking about her behind her back.

"Well, I'll just shut up. I'm just stupid." Once she was agitated, it was not going to be a good visit.

I tried to find a logical explanation for her changing behavior. I thought perhaps her diabetic medication was conflicting with her blood pressure medication. I thought perhaps she was grieving her mother and needs someone to talk to. After she screamed, "I don't need your help! I can catch the bus to go home!" She slammed the car door and walked away.

Maybe she just hates me, I thought.

In my journal, I described my mom's behavior as psychological or maybe neurological. At that time, I didn't know what dementia looked like. I thought it was memory loss. I wasn't aware that dementia often included all these other behavior changes. I would soon realize these other behavior changes are the real challenge to care; not the memory loss.

Years later—after the dementia diagnosis and my subsequent education on the disorder—I ran across a letter I had written to her primary care physician attempting to explain my theories about Mom's changing behaviors and get some help. The letter mentioned confusion about events and timelines. It mentioned a heightened level of agitation and paranoia focused on her house, extreme anger and moodiness, disagreeable when we tried to help her, difficulty paying bills, and not socializing.

After reading the behaviors I had described in the letter years ago, I wondered why no one told me she was practically a case study for dementia. This was my initial attempt to get an explanation which led to a diagnosis of "cognitive impairment, normal for her age." It would be May, nine months later, after my insistence that these behaviors were definitely not "normal" before Mom received a diagnosis that explained everything.

Re: Mary A Jackson (dob: 12/06/37)

[redacted], I believe my mother has reached a need for a different level of treatment to help her to deal with changes in her life. Her current treatment focuses on management of Diabetes, Hypertension and cholesterol which all seem to be under control. I believe she also is struggling with a condition that is more psychological or neurological; however, she is not receiving any treatment. Below, I have described just a semblance of the behavior changes I am concerned about. I would appreciate your use of this information along with her scheduled visit on **August 1** to consider options for treatment.

Expresses confusion about event and when they happened.

Demonstrates a heightened level of confusion and frustration about the house in Fort Gaines.

Demonstrates extreme anger and moodiness.

Very disagreeable when suggestions are made that are intended to be helpful to her. Mostly targeted at family members closest to her.

Constantly says, "I'll just shut up." "I won't say anything again." "Nobody pays me any attention." "I'm stupid, I don't know what I'm talking about." Assumes our comments mean we are disagreeing with her or making her seem like she doesn't know what she's talking about.

Acknowledging that she is confused and having difficulty with some things like paying bills. Noticed that a checkbook dated back to 2010 had several checks (almost entire box) with half written checks. Most had 1 or 2 pieces of information but never completed.

Normal For Her Age

In late summer 2014, the primary care physician referred Mom to a neurologist. I wrote a letter to the doctor to make sure they had comprehensive information. I was always writing letters and emails.

Excerpt from Note: August 15, 2014

This visit is to get a diagnosis for behavior changes displayed by Mother. She is agreeing to come to this visit, referred by her primary doctor, to determine what is going on with her head and why she is having "strange" feelings in her head.

Experienced a black-out episode in late 2011 which resulted in ER visit and three-day hospitalization to run tests. Didn't find a conclusive reason for the episode. Experienced a similar black-out episode about two weeks ago. 911 called but she had stabilized when arrived.

The endocrinologist believes her blood sugar drops in the evening and that is what is causing those episodes. She was taking two types of insulin; he has changed to one which he believes will stabilize her insulin. Prior to that episode, she was living alone in South Georgia since March—late July. Not sure if these episodes have happened during that time.

Had very high blood pressure about two weeks ago but seemed to be one day. That day, she was extremely angry at me and her sister. Doesn't seem to be eating a lot. When suggested that she snack during the day or even drink nutrient supplemental shakes, she becomes extremely angry.

Currently not comfortable with taking her back to her home in South Georgia. Mostly alone there and no support. Need to determine her condition to determine if she can live alone.

Applied to senior facilities to consider moving her to Atlanta closer to daughter and sister. She basically cares for herself: bathing, clothing, eating, cooking, and shopping. Concerned about memory loss and confusion.

She is having extreme difficulty adjusting to growing older. She doesn't socialize outside of her comfort zone.

After the "cognitive impairment, normal for her age" diagnosis, we returned with no explanation and, consequently, no treatment. The behaviors continued and became more pronounced. Mom sat despondently in a room with the lights off. I tried everything to get her out of that negative place. I took her to visit people from her past, thinking that would make her happy. But she mostly sat quietly and didn't socialize.

She complained about pain in different parts of her body. She described shooting pains, pointing to her side and following it around to the other side and up her back. I didn't want to disregard what she was saying, so I made appointments to address all her complaints and the progressing behaviors.

When we finally got to the doctor, she didn't mention the pains. The appointments, rescheduling, and coordination with my job extended the usual two to three weeks of doctor appointments into a decision that Mom couldn't return to her home in South Georgia. I had to move her to Atlanta closer to me.

This Is Called Lewy

We continued with the "normal for her age" diagnosis for several months. The turning point happened one day when Mom was unusually fixated on those pills. She kept picking up the bottles, shaking them, and complaining that she didn't have all her pills. I offered to help with her pills, and she became very agitated with me. I insisted on trying to help her see that she had all her pills. The more I tried, the more agitated she became until finally, it was too much for her. She ran down the hallway throwing the pill bottles across the room, screaming, "Just leave me alone!"

I froze and reached slowly to hit record on my phone so I could remember that this really happened. That's when I knew, this was not "normal for her age." This was something else.

I scheduled another neurological visit. There was only one available appointment, but it was with a neurologist specializing in epilepsy at Emory. I needed answers so I took it.

Dr. Rodriguez tested her and referred her to the Emory Integrated Memory Care Center (IMCC), a newly formed group that specialized in dementia care. In May 2015, the neurological team at the IMCC diagnosed her with Lewy body dementia (LBD, a.k.a. Lewy). Mom was seventy-seven. I think she understood that he had diagnosed her with something but I don't think she understood what it meant. She said, "Well, I'm seventy-seven. I'm going to forget some things."

I remember thinking, *that makes sense*. I knew she needed help, but I didn't understand what it meant either. Until that day, I had never heard of Lewy body dementia.

The IMCC started her on a medication called Aricept (a.k.a. donepezil). Right after the diagnosis, I didn't know what to do. She had LBD, but I didn't know what that meant or how to take care of her and deal with the behaviors.

The IMCC became her new primary care provider. The care focused on her needs considering the dementia. They also assessed my needs as a caregiver. Her behavior and responses were not "strange" to them. The IMCC offered many resources and referred me to the Atlanta Regional Commission BRI program, a telephone-based information and support service for family caregivers. I was connected to information about training for family caregivers, resources to find caregivers, respite care, memory care, devices, tools, and more. I learned about Teepa Snow, a guru in dementia-care techniques, and her Positive Approach to Dementia Care model. [1]

I referred to these positive approach techniques often. All these things helped me understand the adjustments I needed to make as the disease progressed. Honestly, in 2015, I didn't know how life would change for us or what disappointments lay ahead of us. That's why I'm writing this: in the hopes of helping someone else on this journey make the inevitable, difficult decisions.

My advice is to get an exact diagnosis if you know or suspect your loved one has dementia. Make sure they tell you what type of dementia your loved one has. Alzheimer's is the most common, but there is dementia with Lewy bodies, vascular, frontotemporal, and others. Many families try to care for their loved ones without knowing the type of dementia they have.

It's imperative to insist that something is wrong and get a diagnosis.

I described Mom's behaviors perfectly in my journal and still got a "normal for her age" initial diagnosis. Although cognitive impairment is a diagnosis, you should consider when the behavior is no longer "normal". Once you get a diagnosis, make sure all other medical providers are aware of the diagnosis.

---

[1] This content is based on the work of Teepa Snow's Positive Approach to Care® methods and education. https://teepasnow.com/

Chapter 3

GOOD DAYS AND BAD DAYS

The Move to Clairemont

In the fall of 2015, after the LBD diagnosis, Mom was still independent, but she was either very difficult or very pleasant. She was able to take care of her activities of daily living (ADLs).

Operating small kitchen appliances like the coffeemaker or microwave was confusing to her, so she compensated by saying it wasn't working right.

I couldn't take her back to her home because it was three hours away. I had to keep her closer to me. I moved her to an independent senior apartment: Clairemont. I had to furnish her one-bedroom apartment. The kindness and compassion people showed was overwhelming. I encountered many who had their own stories to tell and wanted to help me when they realized I was setting up a place for my mother who had dementia.

Mom and I went to consignment stores and thrift shops to look for items for the apartment. She enjoyed shopping. I brought some smaller items from her house. It was cozy and comfortable.

She had never lived in an apartment building. Change was uncomfortable for her which made it uncomfortable for me. I stayed with her the first two weeks. She understood I didn't live there, and one day, she told me, "You don't have to stay here with me. I know you have a husband."

My advice is to keep your loved one's space simple by avoiding clutter. Include only items that are required. There will be days when you'll need to find things, and the fewer places you have to look, the better.

I don't know what gave me the idea of a camera. Mom was ok, but I knew her situation was unpredictable. I set up three indoor internet-based cameras that allowed me to see the apartment from various angles. The cameras proved to be the best complement to a caregiver. It was inexpensive and worked conveniently from my phone. When she was alone, I could check the cameras to be sure she was moving around safely or that she was sleeping at night.

If I didn't see her on the camera for a while, I called her landline phone. She would appear from her cleaning or wherever to answer the phone which was in view of the living room camera. First thing in the morning and last thing before I went to sleep, I checked the Clairemont camera. If she was sound asleep, I could sleep. I noticed that she still got on her knees and prayed before she went to bed, a memory Lewy hadn't taken.

For about three years, the disease was stable with a slow decline. As the disease progressed, Mom developed repetitive behaviors. She rolled and unrolled her hair in curlers over and over again. She rolled tissue paper over and over. We had to hide a roll so we had some to use for what we really needed toilet tissue for.

She could do a lot of things on her own including going to the bathroom. Aunt Betty and I took her out to shops and restaurants for exercise and monitored social stimulation. I took her to hair appointments, a familiar experience she liked. Shopping was walking through smaller stores like thrift stores where she enjoyed perusing

the aisles. Her favorite outings were Golden Corral, Piccadilly, and Kacey's Country Kitchen.

Aricept helped her to maintain stability with the disease for about three years. I was grateful she didn't have any significant illnesses, not even colds or flu during the time we cared for her at Clairemont.

I'm Going Home

The first several weeks after the move to Clairemont were quite harrowing for me. Mom never tried to walk out of the apartment but often said, "I want to go home." She would ask if Mo (her mother) was at home. Many people told me dementia patients wandered, but Mom never tried, and I felt comfortable she didn't know how to use the elevator to get downstairs, so accessing an exit would be difficult for her. I prayed that was the case.

During the early days of the disease, I didn't usually schedule a caregiver on weekends. Aunt Betty and I took turns visiting her on weekends. One Saturday, I was running late going to Clairemont. I called to check on her, making sure she was just meddling around the apartment and not wandering the hallway. Mom was agitated on the phone. "I'm leaving. I'm going home!"

I pleaded with her to not go home. "Wait for me, ok? I'm on the way right now!"

"Well, you better come on! I'll catch the bus!" Lewy was good at manipulating me into immediate response. She hung up. I continued to call her to be sure she wasn't leaving the apartment. I called several times, but she didn't answer and she wasn't visible on any of the three cameras. If I could get her to answer the phone, I would know she wasn't leaving the building. Lewy played a perfect control strategy on me.

I tried not to get the apartment staff involved, but I panicked and called the security desk. I asked the officer on duty if she could check on Ms. Mary in 409. "Nothing is wrong. She's not answering her phone, and I want to be sure she's ok."

The apartment wasn't assisted living and it wasn't their responsibility to check on residents, but they would do it if the requests weren't frequent. "Sure," she said.

Twenty minutes passed which seemed like two hours. Finally, the security officer called back and said, "Ms. Mary is ok."

I was relieved. "Did, you talk to her? She's not answering the phone."

"Yes. I went to her apartment. She said she was on her way out and she walked with me downstairs." I panicked.

"Mom is *downstairs*?" I imagined her out the door and down the street by then, getting on the bus trying to go home. The MARTA intra-city bus stopped right in front of the building. She often said she would catch the bus and go home. Thoughts of her getting on that bus raced through my head. "Where is she now? Do you see her?"

"Yes, she's here in the lobby."

"*Please* ask her to wait for her daughter. Tell her I'm on the way and don't leave until I get there!"

I think the officer heard the concern in my voice. "Sure, I understand." Without saying it, the officer's tone let me know she understood what I feared and would keep an eye on her. I felt better, but I knew if Lewy took over and Mom got agitated in the lobby, it could end up a public disturbance.

It seemed like every traffic light was red. I proceeded cautiously but as I got closer, I imagined what might be going on in the Clairemont lobby at that moment. When I arrived, Mom was sitting calmly in the lobby with two large tote bags of essentials consisting of rolls of toilet tissue, hair rollers, and a few other insignificant items.

She wasn't agitated as she had been on the phone. I asked her if she wanted to go for a ride with me. She said yes. I didn't mention her earlier plans to leave. As we left the lobby, I looked back at the security guard sitting behind the lobby desk and quietly mouthed, "Thank you."

Mom and I drove through neighborhoods in the Great Lakes and Druid Hills areas, talking about the houses and the people who lived in those houses in Alabama. She always thought we were in Alabama when we rode through Decatur. Riding in the car was often a good experience for her.

After the "I'm going home" incident, I knew I needed a way to track Mom if Lewy convinced her she should catch the bus and go home. I thought about all the Mattie Calls—known as silver alerts in many places—and was terrified of the scenarios that raced through my mind.

As a result, I bought a tracking device called SmartSole shoe insert. It works with GPS monitoring. It was expensive and there was a monthly monitoring fee, but it was worth it for my peace of mind. I placed it in the one pair of shoes I was sure she'd put on. Also, I purchased three small Tile tracker devices. I placed one in the inner liner of her black purse, one on the door keys, and one on the TV remote because we looked for that all the time.

I would have put one on her hair rollers and toilet tissue if I could have determined how to do it. She would have at least one of those items on her if she walked out or if we couldn't find her in the building. Later, I ordered an ID bracelet with her name and medical condition. I gave it to her as a birthday gift so she wouldn't take it off. Fortunately, wandering never became an issue with Mom, but the trackers often helped us find the door keys, her shoes, and the TV remote.

The Flood

At 9:30 AM, I was at work in Marietta, GA. I propped my phone against the cubicle wall behind my computer monitor so I could glance at it occasionally. I waited to see Mom appear on camera. She didn't appear. After a while, I called her landline to check on her.

She appeared on the camera to answer the phone. She was eating breakfast. I told her that Ms. Gwen—the caregiver—would be there soon to visit her.

"I don't know why. I don't need a babysitter," she said as usual. We talked a bit longer and then hung up. I kept my phone on my desk and monitored the apartment until the caregiver arrived. About 10:15 AM, I peeped at the camera again. On the living room camera the carpet floor looked dark, like a shadow. I didn't see Mom.

Maybe it's nothing, I thought and shrugged it off. A few minutes later, I noticed the shadow looked more pronounced as if it was getting bigger. *Oh my God, is that water?*

I called the front desk and asked them to go check her apartment. Before I could get off the phone, I saw several people entering the apartment. Mom would be extremely agitated with all those people in there. The caregiver wasn't there yet, so there was no one to keep her calm.

I jumped in my car and headed to Clairemont. It was about thirty-five minutes away which equates to an hour in Atlanta traffic. When I arrived, all was ok, and Mom was sitting in the fourth-floor hallway with the social worker. Mom had gone into the hallway frantically asking for help. She had called it a fire.

All the commotion agitated her. She kept arguing with the maintenance people, telling them she didn't do anything. The apartment building social worker came upstairs to Mom's apartment, taking her away from the commotion, and focused on keeping her calm.

I was told the toilet had backed up—probably due to toilet tissue—and overflowed. It flowed out into the apartment which is what I saw on the camera. It flooded most of the apartment and into the hallway. I was afraid she'd be asked to leave, but to my surprise, this was not an uncommon occurrence in senior apartment buildings.

The Lady in the Mirror

As the disease progressed, so did the challenges of caring for Mom. The apartment décor became less about decoration and more about safety. One day, Mom, Aunt Betty, and I were talking in the living room. Mom went around the corner into her bedroom. I would peep in if she was gone too long or look at the bedroom camera from my phone so she wouldn't see me watching her. I heard her voice. She was talking to herself. This was not uncommon. The voice got louder and more agitated. I jumped up from my seat and ran toward her to find the agitation's source. I found

Mom standing in the bathroom at the sink. "What's wrong?" I asked.

"Why she keep looking at me?"

"Who?"

"That woman. She keep looking at me!" Mom turned to look at me, I saw the frustration on her face and in the tone of her voice. I realized she was referring to her reflection in the medicine cabinet mirror. It caught me off guard, but I knew not to explain the concept of her reflection.

To deescalate the situation, I agreed with her. "She knows you. She's a very nice lady." Later, Mom would sometimes calmly talk to the lady in the mirror. As her aggressive behaviors grew, I eventually covered all the mirrors in the apartment so the lady in the mirror wouldn't agitate Lewy.

Visiting Johnnie

Although we tried to keep Mom from walking the apartment building hallways, sometimes she just wanted to get out. We let her walk if she was calm, but we watched her inconspicuously or walked with her. At night, the large window at the end of the hall became a wall-sized mirror due to the reflection it made.

At some point, Mom realized there was a lady at the end of the hall that she liked to talk to. In the evenings, she wanted to walk down the hall toward the window. Perhaps it was sundowners—an increased state of confusion starting in late afternoon or at night. The caregiver noticed that she would stand and talk to herself in front of the window next to the Christmas tree.

She liked this lady, and the visits made her happy. One day, Mom said, "I talked to Johnnie. But I don't think she could hear me. I told her she could come over here and stay with me. I'll take care of her."

Mom thought her reflection was her younger sister Johnnie. Many people said they looked a lot like each other. Johnnie lived with her daughter on the other side of town because she too had dementia. Mom and Johnnie didn't see each other as often as the disease progressed. Mom was glad to see Johnnie and talk to her.

"She can hear you. She'll come to sit with you one day," I said. I told the caregiver why Mom liked to go to the end of the hallway. She was visiting her sister.

Although we tried to keep her in the apartment, we agreed to let her walk as long as she was calm. The window was next to the laundry room and an elevator. Other residents thought she was strange when she talked to the window, but the joy she got from the visits far outweighed the whisperings.

To Lie or Not to Lie

I remember the first time Mom asked me where her mother was. This was while Mom lived at Clairemont and was still functioning well. Mom was restless. She paced the apartment. I was her sitter that day, and she was very agitated. She walked up to me and, with desperation in her voice, asked, "Where's Mo? Is she dead?"

She had never asked that before. Mom was with Grandma when she passed. I wasn't at the place in this journey yet where I could lie to my mother, so I reacted as a daughter, not as a Caregiver. I did not lie to my mother. "Yes, she died." I wasn't prepared for the response. Mom reacted as if she had just learned for the first time that her mother, her rock, was gone. She cried uncontrollably.

"She's all I had!" Then the anger. "Nobody told me! I would never do that to you!"

She was furious at me. I wanted her pain to stop. I tried to calm her by reminding her that she was with her mom when she passed, that she'd taken good care of her and Mo loved her so much for that. Over the next two or three years, Mom asked me (sometimes multiple times a day), "Where is Mo? Is she dead? Where's Mo?"

After giving her a truthful response the first few times and witnessing her excruciatingly painful experience, I realized it wasn't good for her to experience the death of her mother over and over again. I began to respond, "She's at work, she'll be home later." Similarly, when she asked about the children, I learned to say, "They're in school." She was usually good with that and went about her business.

I realized it was ok as I wasn't lying to her. I was caring for her, preventing her unnecessary emotional pain. Many families struggle with the blurred line between lying to their loved ones for their benefit and the desire be honest. Some caregivers find it difficult not to convince dementia patients that their loved ones transitioned many years ago, especially if they keep asking for them.

I advise you to consider whether it's better to respond with an answer that will give them comfort and relief or to always tell the truth. We must remember that we're caring for the person. My personal perspective was I would have lied to her every day to make her final days as comfortable as possible. Telling her that her mother was gone was the truth, but it only caused more trauma for her.

When I started answering by telling her that her mother was at work, she wasn't devasted. I wasn't devasted seeing her grieve over and over. To care for a dementia patient, give them comfort in any small way you can. If that means telling them their loved ones are ok, at work or school, or wherever that might be, it's ok. There's no reason to feel guilty.

I Will Sit with You; I'll Walk with You

The evening agitation (sundowning) and hallucinations increased. Often, Mom wouldn't sleep at night. After saying good night to the overnight caregiver, Mom would go to bed. A few hours later, she would awaken and not recognize the woman in her house. This would sometimes turn into hours of trying to calm her and not disturb the neighbors.

When my phone rang at night, I knew it was trouble at Clairemont. I could usually talk to her on the phone and convince her to go back to bed, but sometimes it took hours.

One night, the caregiver couldn't get Mom back to bed. She was agitated and insisted the caregiver get out of her house. The caregiver went into the hallway as I talked to Mom on the phone and watched her on the camera.

We tried many strategies to convince Mom to let the caregiver stay in the apartment that night. We were dealing with Lewy. Finally, I asked the caregiver to appeal to Mom's sense of caring. "Tell her you're sick and ask her to please let you stay. You have nowhere else to go."

The caregiver would've tried anything at that point. The next time Mom told her to get out, she said "Ms. Mary, please don't put me out. I'm sick and I don't have anywhere to go and it's dark. Can I please stay until the morning?"

Mom's demeanor changed, and as we hoped, she replied, "You're sick? Is your momma gonna come get you?"

"No Ma'am. My momma's at work."

Mom sat on the sofa next to the caregiver's chair. "Well, I'll sit with you then."

We didn't get her back to bed right away, but we were thankful she was calm and not putting the caregiver out. We were finally able to get some rest.

My mom had the heart to take care of people. It was her natural inclination. Once, Ms. Versie, Mom's neighbor at Claremont, wasn't feeling well and was walking very slowly. Mom rushed to her, put her arms around her shoulder, and proceeded to walk down the hall with her.

"I'll walk with you. Don't worry, I won't walk too fast," Mom said in the voice of a caregiver. I just stood and observed in amazement. Lewy took her comprehension of many basic things, but Lewy hadn't taken her ability to comprehend another person in need or her desire to help them.

Often, the positive strategy to managing the agitation is understanding who the person was before the disease's progression. I urge caregivers and families to look beyond the horrible behaviors of Lewy and appeal to the person's innate personality that is struggling to win.

Hide and Seek

When I entered the apartment, I looked around for things that may have been misplaced during her activities. Sometimes, I didn't know what I was looking for. I opened kitchen cabinets, the fridge, microwave, oven, looked under the mattress, under the bed, and in closets and drawers.

Sometimes, when she didn't finish her meal, she put it away in the kitchen. Away might be in the kitchen cabinet instead of the refrigerator. Almost anything that would fit was found under the mattress at some point.

One evening, I arrived, and the caregiver and Aunt Betty were there chatting with Mom. One of them asked me, "Do you know where the TV remote is? We've been looking for it and can't find it."

I didn't know where it was. We searched everywhere for the remote. Mom looked too. We had lost that remote many times, but this time it was nowhere to be found. We even went through the trash, thinking maybe she had thrown it away.

Finally, Mom came out of her bedroom, holding the remote in her hand, "Y'all looking for this?"

Where had she hidden it? We had looked everywhere. To this day, we don't know. Eventually, I taped a Tile tracker on the remote using a lot of masking tape so she wouldn't remove it. The tracker helped us find the remote many times.

This is one reason I advise families to make their loved one's space as simple and uncluttered as you can. If there are fewer places to hide things, it makes it easier to find things.

Cooking

When Mom moved to Clairemont, she was still able to perform all her ADLs, including cooking easy meals. One morning, the caregiver arrived about 10 AM as scheduled. I scheduled the caregiver to arrive at 10 AM because usually, Mom had showered by then. I didn't want her to be in the shower when the caregiver arrived, she could slip and fall trying to get to the door.

As the caregiver approached her apartment, there was a burned smell in the hallway. She knocked on the door, concerned about what she might find. Mom took a little longer than usual, but she finally opened the door. The caregiver said, "Good morning, Ms. Mary."

"Morning," she replied, as if to say, "it's you again."

The caregiver, still in the hallway, looked past Mom into the apartment. "I just came by to visit. Is everything ok?" The burned smell was more pronounced after the door was opened.

"I didn't do anything!" Mom said as she stepped aside. The caregiver entered the apartment. She noticed the window directly across from the door was open, which was unusual. Then, she noticed the charred toast on the stove in the small kitchen immediately to the right, which explained the smell in the hallway.

When I arrived at Clairemont that evening after work, the apartment administrator stopped me at the front desk to inform me of the incident. The burnt toast had set off the alarm and alerted the security officer. I knew this meant the apartment management was aware that Mom may not be able to live there independently. We were required to provide help for her to make sure she met the qualifications to live there.

Mom could afford the apartment with her own income and it was in a safe area of Decatur. I wanted her to be able to stay there.

This was the first indication that Mom needed more help with meal preparation.

The Casserole Dish

One evening after work, I arrived at Clairemont to discover an odd smell in the kitchen. I followed the smell and opened the oven door. A white plastic storage dish designed to look like a casserole dish was almost completely melted. I understood how she thought it was a real casserole dish.

My anxiety increased.

The oven was turned off but still hot. I almost burned my hand as I reached in to get the dish. It suddenly occurred to me that Mom might have burned herself if she had tried to get the dish out. I checked her arms and hands to see if she had any burns.

She was sitting quietly on the sofa. I knew to not show my anxiety or respond like something bad had happened. I was so relieved to not find any burns. How could she not have burned herself? Apparently, it started to smoke, and she was able to turn it off. She probably didn't remember that she had put the dish in the oven. I don't remember what she was trying to cook in that dish.

After the casserole dish incident, I knew I had to remove anything that might encourage her to want to cook. That's what she'd always done since she was old enough to stand at the stove. Little by little, we had to take away those things that defined her.

I didn't want to take that from her. I needed to find another solution. I needed to find another way for her to cook safely. Until then, I told her something was wrong with the stove.

"They need to fix that stove. It doesn't work right. Don't use it until they fix it." I made it someone else's fault, not hers, to get her buy-in. She agreed that something was wrong with it and stayed away from the stove for a while.

To mitigate the risks of cooking and to help her maintain some semblance of independence, I bought a manual dial microwave and an auto-shutoff electric kettle for her morning cup of coffee. For a while, she could use the microwave to heat pre-made food. Mom could fix her own breakfast with croissants, a container of yogurt, fresh fruit, and a cup of coffee.

Because she was a cook by trade, she always tried to do more. She started melting cheese on sliced bread in the microwave. One day, I found a badly burned croissant in the microwave. She had turned the dial as far as it would go and the twenty minutes of microwaving had burned the croissant to a crisp. I taped the temperature dial so it was set to low. That way, even if she turned the time dial all the way, the temp was low and probably wouldn't burn her bread.

I tried to show her how to turn the knob to the right just a little, not all the way.

"I didn't turn it. I know how to do that. We used to do that in the kitchen!" Mom had worked in the hospital kitchen and the Marriott Marquis kitchen commissary. She knew her way around a kitchen. She clearly understood I was insulting her abilities. After that "talking to", I clearly understood that she was my momma and I needed to find a way to prevent the cooking incidents without insulting her.

Mr. Ralph

I think the casserole dish incident scared Mom. I put childproof covers on the stove knobs so she couldn't turn the stove on. Eventually, she figured out how to remove them during her cleaning, but it bought us some time. Later, I turned off the power to the oven from the fuse box. We started putting pre-made meals and snack foods in the kitchen.

She liked salads, sandwich biscuits, fresh melons, and fried chicken. We also kept finger foods that she could easily snack on like oranges, apples, mixed nuts, and crackers.

For more balanced meals, we brought dinners with vegetables in Styrofoam containers and placed them in the fridge. Piccadilly served meals in the kitchen downstairs daily for residents, but she wasn't able to go downstairs on her own. Honestly, I feared she would get agitated around the other residents and they would question whether she should live there. The senior community, like high school, had cliques. Dementia behaviors were not well received, so we tried to provide for her needs and avoid interaction with the apartment tenants and staff.

Piccadilly delivered the meals to her apartment if I requested.

Meal delivery became somewhat of an unpredictable event. Mom opened the door and Mr. Ralph, from Piccadilly, said "I got your meal, Ms. Jackson."

That's when it started. Once, she replied, "That ain't mine!" And she wouldn't take it. He tried explaining that she had ordered it. That didn't fly either. She insisted she hadn't ordered anything, argued that it wasn't hers, and demanded he figure out who's it was. Somehow, he got her to take it, but she put it in the fridge to hold for whomever it belonged to because it most certainly wasn't hers.

Another day, Mom opened the door and Mr. Ralph said, "I got your meal, Ms. Jackson."

"Okay, thank you. How much do I owe you?" Mom was happy to receive the meal. She was in a good mood that day and went to get her purse to pay him for it. He explained that she already paid for it. She went on and on thanking him and talking about this and that. Of course, he just wanted to drop off the meal and move on to the next delivery, but he was always patient with her.

Sometimes, Aunt Betty or I were sitting in the background and were quite entertained by the new attempt to deliver the food and the bantering between Mom and Mr. Ralph. Mr. Ralph soon realized he never knew what to expect at apartment 409.

Food Is Love

Before LBD, Mom expressed her love for family by cooking big, delicious meals for us. I saw her offer meals to people if she thought they were hungry. Food made her happy, I suppose because her family didn't have an abundance of it growing up.

One evening, when I arrived after work, she said, "You hungry? I cooked!" She pulled items out of the refrigerator, showing me what she had cooked. I think she pulled out everything in the fridge. "I got some chicken, some peas, some of this, some of that. Fix you a plate if you want."

It was several food items Aunt Betty and I had placed in the fridge for her. Having a lot of food in the kitchen to offer seemed to be a good, familiar feeling for her. I knew accepting the offer would make her feel great, so I fixed myself a plate and ate.

Grocery Shopping

Mom was known for taking a long time perusing the grocery store aisles, carefully selecting essentials within a limited budget. Despite the dementia, shopping was still a familiar activity for her. We wanted her to be able to enjoy shopping and feel independent, but we needed to control the activity.

I learned to avoid mega-size grocery stores like Walmart. Her neighborhood had a small Kroger grocery store. Mom never drove a car, so taking her to the grocery store was a routine activity. My role used to be patiently waiting as she perused all the aisles. Now, my role was patiently monitoring.

She retrieved a shopping cart and began the familiar task of scanning aisles, picking up items and inspecting them. I'm sure she used to consider cost, but with dementia, it was mostly the routine she was experiencing. This wasn't about grocery shopping but allowing her to go through the habitual exercise as I covertly followed along.

I checked the cart and discreetly removed items we didn't want her to have in the kitchen. She picked up things she always bought like a five-pound bag of flour to fry chicken or make her delicious biscuits. She picked up a carton of eggs because she always bought eggs. I discreetly removed them while casually talking about all the stuff we needed to get. I made sure the cart had some items we could actually use.

One day, I couldn't remove the eggs without her seeing me, so I tried to put them on the side when we got to the checkout. She saw the eggs (not realizing I had put them there) and put them back on the belt. We bought eggs that day.

I advise families to provide your loved ones with familiar experiences as often as possible. What did they enjoy doing before the disease? What were their routines? Allow them to do things independently as long as they can by increasing the controls around them. This isn't always easy to do, I know.

Dignity and Incontinence

I once read that it's not the incontinence that robs them of their dignity, it's the way others react to them because of the incontinence. This is a hard topic, but I want to address it because everyone I've talked to has dealt with incontinence alongside dementia.

Again, this is not from a medical perspective. I supposed the medications—maybe the Januvia for diabetes, the Metformin, or the Aricept—started to give Mom diarrhea. She could go to the bathroom on her own but accidents happened. Even with dementia, she understood the embarrassment of this.

When we offered to help, it agitated her. We told her it was ok and bought her Depends. She threw them across the room. "I don't need that! I never peed in the bed!"

We lined the bed heavily. She disappeared into the bathroom to clean herself up when it happened, and we just kept the soiled clothes and linens washed. A little vinegar in the wash helped, and I often handwashed soiled underwear first. A few times, I just threw them away. I would rather buy more. We never scolded her or even mentioned that she had done anything wrong. It was important to respect her dignity.

As the disease progressed, the accidents occurred more often. Eventually, she only remembered the action of toileting. The closet or floor beside the bed became the bathroom. This precipitated the need to move from Clairemont and increase her care.

Incontinence is a common source of agitation. Once Mom was in long-term care facilities, agitation due to toileting was used to justify that she needed medication. Setting a toileting schedule, regular changing, and a dignified approach are more positive strategies to manage the situation before medication.

I learned in the caregiver workshop that toileting is a private action learned at an early age. Your loved one may feel embarrassed that someone, especially the opposite sex, must help with toileting. You should never scold your loved one when accidents happen. Blame the dementia.

The Next Level of Care

With the cooking incidents, increased agitation, and incontinence, the level of care needed had definitely increased. Toward the end of 2018, into early 2019, Mom needed twenty-four-hour care, but she was still in the independent senior apartment. She was mobile, but incontinence and the hallucinations were more frequent, so she was a risk for walking the hallways at night.

I increased care so someone was with Mom all the time, including overnight. Between myself, Aunt Betty, and two caregivers, we covered every shift. It was not without sacrifice. Between my full-time job and caring for Mom, I wasn't home a lot, and the cost of two caregivers was high even with Medicaid assistance.

It became more difficult to take care of her at Clairemont without impacting other residents. I knew it was only a matter of time before management required her to leave. Some neighbors started complaining about her behaviors. I started looking at other options for care anticipating that inevitable decision. I didn't know what disappointments were in front of us as we entered the world of long-term care.

Chapter 4

DEMENTIA AND DOCTORS

Communicating with Medical Staff

Doctor appointments were challenging. I never knew if she would cooperate so we could get there on time. I had to manage the visit to be sure the doctor considered all the dementia behaviors and changes we saw. I had to do it so Mom didn't hear us talking about her. As I suggested in the "Journaling" section in Chapter 2, keep notes of all the information you want the doctors to consider during the visit. I covertly signaled to the nurse that I needed to speak with or provide notes for the doctor's review before the doctor came into the room.

If I answered the questions when the doctor came in, Mom might get agitated about talking for her. She often shouted, "No one's paying me any attention!" To keep her calm during the limited amount of time we had with the doctor, I needed to communicate about her condition outside of her presence.

If your loved one gets distressed when you and the medical providers discuss him/her, I strongly suggest writing it down. Doctors usually review the case prior to meeting with the patient. You can email the notes before the visit or hand them to the nurse for the doctor to review prior to coming into the room.

The way the patient care team engaged with her determined whether it was going to be a good or bad visit. On a good day, Mom wanted to talk and socialize. Some care staff engaged with her well, others were about business and didn't connect with her. That was the first indication it might be a bad visit.

While looking at the intake screen, not at her, the nurse would ask, "Ms. Jackson, have you had any aches or pains?"

In her sarcastic tone, she'd say, "I worked all my life. I grew up working in the fields. I guess I would have some aches and pains." Coordinating doctor appointments and sick leave from my job was a challenge, so I was willing to try anything to get the care provider on the same page to accomplish an effective visit. I typed up a note that I would covertly put in front of them. I wanted them to know Mom had dementia, and to consider that as they engaged with her. This is an excerpt of a note I wrote to take with us to her doctor appointments:

> *To Mary Jackson's Physician Care Team:*
>
> *I kindly ask that you be aware that my mother has Dementia and please consider that when communicating with her and, more importantly, in determining treatment for her.*
>
> *Her relationship with her doctors is very important to her, so please help me to help you by showing patience with her.*
>
> *Thank you kindly*
> *Bonnie M Roache (daughter)*

Social Visits

Mom was usually irritated during the rides to the doctor's office. When we entered the office and she was recognized by the nurse, she became a social butterfly.

"Hey Ms. Jackson, you're back to visit us again?"

"Yes, I had to go down home."

"Well, it's good to see you, Ms. Jackson," the Nurse said as she did her vital checks on Mom. "How have you been?"

"All right…I guess. It's good to be seen." Then she would carry conversations with other staff in the office, waving her hands as she spoke. "Hey, how you doing? You look like you working hard back there!"

"Yes ma'am," they would reply. She talked and laughed, and they laughed as if they appreciated the break in monotony. Then there were the staff members she insisted were our relatives.

"I know you might be kin to us. Where you from?" Once we encountered an intake nurse who had heard of our little hometown, Fort Gaines. "I know about Fort Gaines, I'm from Blakely." Mom smiled recognizing the name of the town and insisted she was "kin" to us. The nurse went along with it. She knew it would help her do what she needed to do.

Those were "good" days. Mom loved the visits on "good" days. I realized going to the doctor was a social outlet. The medical talk happened after we stepped outside the room. As we left the office, I allowed her to socialize and act like she was a local celebrity while I took care of the administrative details and scheduled the next appointment.

Other Medical Conditions and Dementia

Mom had been going to Dr. Flowers, her endocrinologist, for many years after her diabetic diagnosis. They were the same age and they'd both grown older over the years. She'd done a good job managing her diabetes by losing weight and preparing healthy meals for herself.

Mom managed her medications and self-administered her insulin, keeping a log of her blood sugar readings three times a day.

As the disease progressed, those entries became random and inconsistent. During one visit with Dr. Flowers after the dementia diagnosis, I brought the glucose testing machine with us so the nurse could pull the readings from the machine rather than rely on what Mom had written. At least that was my plan.

The visit started with the usual greetings and Mom socializing with the staff as they checked her in and took her vitals. I covertly mentioned to the nurse, "I have her machine so you can get her blood sugar readings for the doctor." She nodded in agreement, but she never asked for the machine. The doctor came in and asked for the readings on paper. Mom handed him several crinkled pieces of paper with random numbers.

I said, "I brought her machine with us so you can see her actual readings. That may be better. As you can tell, some things have changed." I gave him a look affirming I knew the readings weren't reliable and waited for his concurrence.

Dr. Flowers replied, "Oh no, that's fine, we don't need it." I couldn't understand how he made decisions based on data written by my mom at that point. The medical staff acknowledged that she was obviously more confused, and they were aware of the dementia diagnosis.

"Should we reconsider the dosage of her Metformin considering she's lost a significant amount of weight? The medication's reaction to her body weight may be different."

He agreed to lower the Metformin dosage, but it seemed more about getting past my request than determining whether that was the best course. Dr. Flowers and the staff seemed caring but didn't consider her diabetic treatment needs as her weight and her ability to self-monitor changed. My requests created conflict between me and the staff as my questions weren't well received.

Mom had a fixation with Dr. Flowers as her doctor. She had been going to him for many years. He was familiar to her and she was familiar with him. If I changed her doctor, Mom would be furious with me. I dealt with it a little while longer. Eventually, we changed to an endocrinologist referred by the IMCC primary care team.

As the disease progressed, I thought the care for her other critical conditions—diabetes and heart disease—should be considered with her changes in dementia-care treatment. Surprisingly, most doctors did not reassess her treatment unless I requested it.

Initiate the conversation. Make them accountable in considering your loved one's changes due to dementia and how those changes might impact their current care plans. If your loved one's medical providers aren't willing to consider the impact of dementia changes on their care plan, then consider a doctor that specializes in geriatric care.

Getting-Ready Routine

It was a challenge trying to schedule Mom's appointments. I didn't want to miss one because a reschedule might be months later. The routine of getting ready was unpredictable. I couldn't tell Mom about an appointment and expect her to remember to get ready the next day. She could not consistently comprehend what day or time it was. Early morning appointments were more challenging, so I learned to not schedule early morning appointments.

On the day of, we would start talking about the appointment so we could keep her focused on getting ready. The getting-ready routine took a long time. It's hard to explain why it took so long. It was like a continuous never-ending loop of activities.

"Mom, let's get your shoes so we can go to your appointment. We don't want to be late"

"Where are they?"

We looked for the shoes. I found one under the bed, the other in the closet. "Here are your shoes, Mom. Put these on."

Five minutes later, "Mom that's the wrong shoe. What did you do with the other shoes I gave you?"

"I don't know. Where are they?"

I looked for the other shoes and finally found them in the bathroom.

"Mom, let's put on your shoes. I notice one sock is off. Where's the other sock?"

Finally, we would have two matching shoes and somewhat matching socks. The two socks didn't match, but they were close enough. "Let me help you put on your shoes." We finally got into the hallway to leave.

I realized I couldn't take her out without something to keep her warm. "It's a little cool out. Let's get a sweater."

"I don't need a sweater," she replied.

"Well, will you carry it with you? Wait right here while I go back inside to get your sweater."

I went inside and quickly found a sweater. As I headed back toward the hallway, she was back inside the apartment. I handed her the sweater expecting her to follow me to the hallway. Instead, she went into the bedroom. I tried to get her to the hallway. "Let's go, Mom. You have an appointment." I tried not to agitate her because if she was agitated, it was *game over.*

"I don't have an appointment!"

"Well, will you go for a ride with me, Mom? Where's the sweater?"

"I don't know anything about a sweater!"

Finally, I found the sweater on the bed, picked up her purse, picked up my purse, got the appointment papers, the door keys, etc., walked into the hallway and stood there with the door open. Eventually, she came out, too, and we finally left.

Missed Appointment

Getting Mom to an 8:15 AM appointment was a bad idea, but I didn't know that at the time. I scheduled an important appointment; I don't recall why it was important, but I recall it was difficult to schedule. This was prior to the dementia diagnosis.

We arrived downtown at Emory Midtown about 8:15 AM. I parked in the deck as we usually did. Had I been thinking, I would have let the valet park the car instead. It took another fifteen minutes to park and walk across the bridge to the main building to catch the elevator to the seventh floor. We arrived at the doctor's office about 8:35 AM for an 8:15 AM appointment.

The nurse said, "You're too late. The doctor can't see you today. You'll have to reschedule."

"I know we're late, Ma'am, but can he please see us? I don't know when I'll be able to get her back here. We can wait if he can see us later."

"I'm sorry, Ma'am, you'll have to reschedule." Mom's challenging behaviors were still new to me then. I'd done all I could to get there on time, but I couldn't force her to move any faster.

I felt defeated.

Standing at the desk, tears came to my eyes as I hoped the nurse might fit us into the schedule. I'm sure my voice indicated I was upset. Mom sensed something was wrong and walked up to the desk beside me.

"It's gonna be all right." I don't think she understood we'd missed the appointment, but she understood I was upset.

The Woman on the Bench

We had missed the appointment, so Mom and I left the office and went back downstairs to the main lobby. The magnitude of the changes Mom was going through, and the difficulty of scheduling what used to be routine appointments, was sinking in.

"Sit right here on the bench a moment. I'll be right back."

"All right," she agreed. I think I just needed to breathe, and I didn't want to cry in front of her if tears came. Instead, I tried to salvage the day by seeing if another doctor could see her. Maybe there was a cancellation.

That didn't work out. Standing slightly behind her so she couldn't see me, I kept my eye on her sitting on the bench across the lobby.

Suddenly, I stopped trying to fix the missed appointment. I just looked at her sitting on the bench. I saw her vulnerability.

I realized the woman sitting on that bench was completely dependent on me at that moment. Not that I was contemplating it, but I wondered what would happen if I never came back to that bench. What would she do? How long would she sit there? Would she remember she was waiting for me? How long would it take someone to notice she was alone and needed help? Could she give them information about who she was, an address, or phone number?

She was comfortable sitting there because I had asked her to. She trusted me. I knew she needed me and that our roles of mother and daughter had switched. I would be there for her. That day made me aware that I needed to get an ID bracelet for her. Something that could provide a contact number and her condition.

Chapter 5

THE FACILITIES

Memory Care

Before Mom moved to a memory care facility, I vetted them thoroughly and met with the caregivers on her wing. Everyone presented a caring and professional image. I was afraid about her adjustment to a new environment. She moved into her new room at the memory care on May 28, 2019. No one ever came to the room to be sure she was moved in and had what she needed or to help her acclimate to a new environment. I expected someone to meet with me to go over her medications, her diet, what foods she liked, and understand who she was without LBD.

I assumed there was an orientation process to be sure the new resident wasn't afraid and got settled in their first day. This wasn't the first day of college apparently. There was no orientation. So, I spent the first night with her in memory care.

I don't think the staff knew I was there. No one checked on her during her first night. The next day, I requested to speak with the director. He came to the room and probably didn't realize I had been there overnight.

"What can I do for you?"

"Is there going to be an orientation of some type to get her acclimated and settled?"

"What do you mean?"

"I assumed the kitchen would want to know what food she likes, the recreational staff would want to know what activities she might like, the care team would want to know something about her as a person so they know how to talk to her."

He admitted they didn't have a process, but he accepted the profile I had typed up with this information and said he would share it would the staff.

I selected this memory care because it had wide walkable hallways and neighborhoods with living room, kitchen, and dining areas. The living room area had a TV, sofa, and chairs and the dining room had several tables. The kitchen was modern with real appliances but wasn't used for cooking. The stove wasn't functional, and the refrigerator was locked, understandably.

Mom walked about freely without being told she couldn't go into the hallway, like at Clairemont. I was so relieved when she adjusted well. She walked the halls, and I was told she even walked outside her neighborhood, talked to people, and even got snacks from the snack bar. Mom ate peacefully at the table with the other residents. I was there almost every day and observed that she adjusted well. She did exactly what I hoped she would do.

Unfortunately, the facility didn't adjust to her LBD behaviors. She became agitated during personal changing or showering.

This Is My Neighborhood

I was visiting Mom at memory care about three weeks after she moved in. I was relieved that she walked around looking and getting to know the neighborhood area. I sat in the corner of the living room area checking emails or something on my phone when the sound of a woman's voice caught my attention. The woman spoke and laughed loudly with another staff member, I assumed. She got louder as she got closer.

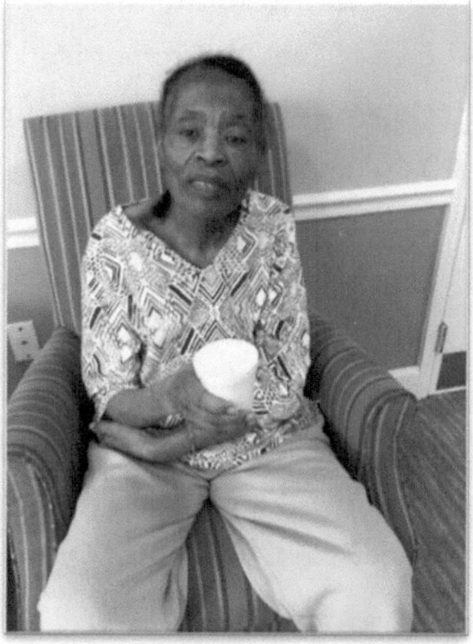

It was a staff member bringing the lunch trays to the neighborhood kitchen. I remember thinking, *That's very loud to come into this area where people with dementia live.*

Based on my training, I knew loud talking and laughing could be scary to someone living with dementia. I went back to my email surfing until I heard the loud voice with a slight Caribbean accent.

"Come on Momma. Get out of the way! Move Momma!"

Then I heard a familiar but stressed voice. "I didn't do anything!"

I looked up from my phone and realized the familiar voice was Mom.

"Come on Momma!" the staff lady said again. I couldn't see Mom behind the wall of the kitchen area, but I could see the source of the loud talking and laughing. She stood at the entryway to the kitchen with a rolling tray of plates trying to get into the kitchen where Mom was.

I went over to the lady. "What's the problem?"

"This tray is hot, and she needs to move so I can put this tray in there."

I turned to Mom and extended my arm to gently lock around hers. "Mom, you're not working in the kitchen today. Let's let Ms. Pat (I made up a name for the woman) work in the kitchen today. You're off today, why don't you come over here with me."

Maybe it was because I was her daughter or maybe it was my approach, but she calmed down and walked out of the kitchen with me. As I walked away, arm locked with Mom's, and looked back at the staff lady. It was a look that said, "*This* is how you remove a dementia patient from a situation, not holler at them."

Later, I said to her, "You know you might scare them. She didn't understand. She thought you were fussing at her."

The lady said, "They understand! I'm just trying to do my job." She whispered something else under her breath. I had offended her by calling out her bad behavior. It's ironic that she easily spoke to my mom and the other residents in a scolding tone, but when I scolded her, it made her feel bad. I was disappointed that an employee of a memory care facility didn't empathize with the residents.

Mom had been looking around the kitchen. She was a cook by trade and kitchens were familiar to her. That was what I wanted her to do. That was her home and it was designed to allow dementia residents to walk around safely.

That's why anyone and everyone working with dementia patients in any capacity should know how to interact with them. The kitchen staff, the ambulance drivers, the maintenance workers, and even the visiting guests should be cognizant of the environment once you enter their world.

A Detrimental Decision

Mom moved to memory care on May 28th. After three to four weeks, the staff began talking to me about giving Mom medication to keep her calm during showering. I was aware that medications could cause other problems, and I didn't want her to be sedated. She walked around the facility very well, and I didn't want medication to make her unstable, contribute to falls, or cause other side effects.

I hadn't been informed nor had I observed agitation at a level that warranted medication. I visited every day, and there had been no mention of anything out of the norm for a memory care facility. Per my awareness, the agitation was normal but not out of control or dangerous. I asked them to consider other non-pharmaceutical approaches during showering and toileting.

They described a medication that would be rubbed on her inner wrists: Ativan, an antianxiety medication. I agreed they could use this as needed. They wanted to give it to her on a regular basis. I was naive to believe facilities would be interested in using other positive approaches to care.

The memory care facility recommended that Mom have an evaluation with their psychiatric consultant. I scheduled the appointment with the psychiatric nurse for later in July as was recommended. I thought we were on the same page.

Beginning the week of July 6, I received a call at work every day with various reports including, "Your mom won't let us change her" and "Your mom was agitated when they tried to shower her." The nursing staff said she was keeping me informed as I requested. I'm sure she started a daily call to make her point that Mom required regular medication.

These weren't situations that warranted a call to a family member. These were all common memory care services. On the fourth day, I received a call at 1 PM informing me that Mom had hit another resident and was being sent out for evaluation via ambulance. She said that was the policy.

They were sending Mom out of the facility because she tried to pick up a glass of water, but it belonged to the other resident. She reportedly hit the other resident on her head. She hadn't been aggressive toward any other resident before that I was aware.

"Are Mom and the other person ok?"

"Yes, there was no injury. Your mom isn't agitated at the moment."

Since she was calm, I asked, "Can I take her to the hospital myself?"

"She has to leave immediately. If you aren't here in twenty minutes, we'll have to send her by ambulance."

Of course, I got there in twenty minutes. When I arrived at the memory care, Mom was calmly sitting with the financial manager at the memory care whom she talked to often because she was nice to her. Mom walked out of the memory care with me that day to get a psychiatric evaluation at the ER as I was told was required per the facility's policy. I thought we would get an assessment and be back that same day.

We spent three days in the Wellstar Hospital Psychiatric Ward waiting for the evaluation to be conducted by hospital staff. We waited, and I worked my project manager job from a straight chair with a makeshift office because I refused to leave her there alone.

She was not uncontrollable per the hospital notes, and although the hospital tried to release her, the memory care would not allow her to return until the psychiatric assessment was done with an order for medication.

The tests showed a UTI, which could have explained agitation. But the memory care wasn't looking for an answer. They only wanted an order from a doctor to allow them to give her medication.

I didn't understand what was going on at the time but I would later find out the memory care staff's ulterior motive. I didn't know what the psychiatric evaluation entailed.

During this process, I asked the memory care for a copy of her records so I could see documented incidents leading up to their request to medicate her. I received a single page of clinical notes consisting of three entries:

- 5/28 – Mom was admitted
- 6/17 – Daughter met with hospice service
- 7/11 – The incident resulting in Mom being sent out of the facility

The facility records had no documented incidents in between her admission to memory care and the facility's attempt to give her medication. I was there often and no one had communicated to me that there were any behaviors warranting a need for medications.

So, what warranted the request for behavior medication treatment? Where was the attempt to collaborate with the family? Where was the effort to make the best decision to care for the person and fight the disease? Where was the positive approach to care?

Resident's Name Mary Jackson Apartment # 310

Clinical Notes

Date	Time	Document clinical notes/progress records. Include your signature and title at the end of the note.
5/28/19	2p	Resident was admitted on 5/28/19 by via daughter. Resident walked into the community talking getting adjusted to new environment. She has NKA Allergies
6/7/19	7pm	Daughter present & spoke to Aberdeen Hospice [redacted] regarding her mother's meds & BS - 314. Resident is asymptomatic [illegible] hyperglycemia. Hospice will follow up w/ resident this weekend. [redacted] RN
7/11/19	1pm	Resident Ms Jackson was sitting at the dinner table with resident [redacted] Ms Jackson asked Ms. [redacted] for her cup. When Ms. [redacted] refused Ms. Jackson with an open hand hit the back of her head. No injuries noted. No bleeding. Ms. Jackson was immediately escorted to her apt. & staff stayed with her until her daughter arrived. Families & MD's of both residents notified. Ms. Jackson was taken to [illegible] ER @ Wellstar Cobb & from there to Ridgeview Mental/Behavioral Hospital for evaluation & treatment. Daughter refused EMS. [illegible] RN
7/23/19	5pm	Ms. Jackson was transferred from Ridgeview to Wellstar Cobb ICU unit 7/22/19 due to sepsis. Will monitor & call Cobb Hospital for follow-up. [redacted] RN

LBD and First-Generation Antipsychotics

On July 13, 2019, the psychiatric facility, Ridgeview, had a room for her. *Finally!* We arrived there, she by ambulance, and I followed by car. I signed forms as her power of attorney (POA), adding a statement saying no experimental treatment should be conducted and I should be notified of any medications she was given.

That was not acknowledged. The facility would not let me behind the closed doors.

Until that moment, I didn't realize I wouldn't be able to access my mom except during limited visiting hours: one to two hours, three days a week, and no weekends. I explained that her LBD diagnosis meant she couldn't make decisions for herself, and I needed access so I could speak for her. I didn't realize this was a mental health and drug rehabilitation facility.

Over the next few days, I called Ridgeview at least three times a day asking how she was doing, what she was doing, and if she was afraid. I pleaded with the staff to allow me to see her since I was her POA and authorized to make decisions in her best interest.

No exceptions were made, and I couldn't speak to her on the phone.

I left numerous messages for her caseworker. Whenever I received a call back, I wrote down what they told me. I wrote that they gave her Risperidone and Haldol. These are antipsychotics generally used to treat schizophrenia and bipolar disorder. I did not know that at the time.

The first visit was two hours. Mom seemed ok. The nurse was nice and said Mom talked to her and told her the names of her children, John and Bonnie. She told me that another lady was crying, and Mom comforted her, telling her it would be ok. I was there every time visitation was allowed, but it was usually only an hour and a half. Seven days after admission, I arrived and found Mom in a Geri chair.

She couldn't open her eyes. She murmured, "I'm all right." The staff said she couldn't feed herself.

Her condition concerned me. Visits were not allowed on Sundays, so I called and left unreturned messages. I had to stop them from giving her those medications.

I wrote a letter based on my authority as Mom's POA stating that the facility had to stop giving Mom medications which made her unresponsive, changing her state from alert to tranquilized. She was heavily sedated. I planned on giving the letter to the staff at my 9 AM visit the next day.

The morning of my visit, my phone rang about 7 AM. "Ms. Roache, we could not wake your mom this morning. An ambulance has been called to take her to the hospital" I was frantic.

When I arrived at the hospital ER, the ambulance had not arrived. Finally, someone lead me to the ER bay #2. Mom was slumped over and unconscious. No one tending to her seemed to have a sense of urgency so I felt everything was under control.

The ER nurse said, "Her vitals are looking better, her BP is going up."

I thought, *She's ok. They'll get fluids in her and she'll wake up. This is just another one of the syncope episodes like she had in the past.* I stood at her bedside in the small ER bay as nurses talked about other things. The doctor came in and everyone was calm. Mom was stable.

Then a tall middle-aged Caucasian man came over and introduced himself as the doctor. He asked me what the decision was if her heart stopped. He said, "I'm not saying there's anything to worry about. We always have to ask the question."

I understood. The same question was asked when I admitted her to the memory care a few weeks prior. I understood the risks of chest compressions but decided I would give her a chance to live. "She's full code."

I couldn't say anything else. I didn't understand how we'd gotten to this day, this place, this unfathomable situation. Mom did exactly what we wanted her to do. She adjusted to her new environment. The memory care didn't adjust to her. Normal dementia agitation should not have led to this.

The next thing I remember, the nurse's tone changed to concern, "Ms. Jackson! Ms. Jackson! What's going on? *What's going on?*"

Just like that, there was a code blue, and I was led away from the room. Several people ran toward me into the room in a blue slow-motion blur. Even the sounds were blurred. I could not believe what was happening. Thoughts raced through my mind. *I can't lose her now! How did we get to this?* Was that the result of trying to get a cup of water and normal dementia agitation?

Mom went into cardiac arrest. Her heart stopped twice. Because I requested full code, they started her heart, and she was put on life support.

July 20, 2019

Ridgeview Institute
Smyrna, GA

Re: Mary A Jackson

I am requesting approval to visit my mother on an agreed schedule outside the regular visiting hours. The reason for this is because Mother is unable to speak for herself. I am her legal power of attorney for medical and other decisions. It is imperative that I have access to visit her to ensure her best interests are being considered.

On Saturday night, July 13, 2019 at approximately 10pm, my mother, Mary A Jackson was admitted to Ridgeview from the ER Psych ward at Cobb Hospital. This was at the request of [redacted] Memory Care Center for an evaluation to determine medication management for dementia behaviors.

She moved into [redacted] on May 27. For the next six weeks, it was observed that Mom was adjusting well, walking about freely, and socializing with other residents and staff as reported by staff members. She demonstrated agitation mostly during toileting and showering. However, this was not all the time. The Aberdeen nurse reported no incidents or agitation when she visited 3 times a week until July 8. Some staff members also told me that they didn't have any problems with her.

PC policy required psychiatric assessment over 3-4 days before she would be admitted back. As a result of that, she was admitted to Ridgeview. On Saturday night, July 20, as her POA, I was not allowed to visit her except during very limited visiting hours. I called numerous times and requested information on her treatment, what medications she was being given, and I was given different information.

On Tuesday, first visiting opportunity, and Wednesday, she was alert, talking, and calm. I was told she became agitated during toileting mostly. By Thursday, my aunt was not allowed to see her because she did not have the patient ID. Next visiting time was Saturday. I visited and Mom was highly sedated. She could talk about 15 minutes but could not stay awake. I pleaded with Ridgeview to let me visit her Sunday. The doctor denied. I was told that she was being given Resperidone 2-3 times a day. On Monday, I expressed my concerns with her sedated state to PC Nurse and ED. Nurse visited her on Monday already and said she observed the same thing. Mom was not able to walk or feed herself or even eat when they tried to feed her.

On Tuesday morning, she was rushed to ER with very low heart rate, in hypothermia state. During ER visit she suffered cardiac arrest and was put on life support.

While Mom recovered in the hospital, the financial manager at the memory care who had sat with Mom, called to check on her. "Bonnie, why did you take her to that psychiatric facility?"

I was confused why she would ask that. "Because you all required me to."

She emphatically denied their facility would require that. I assured her that's what the hospital and I were told during the three days we spent in the psych ward. "The memory care staff would *not* allow the hospital to release Mom back to the memory care until she was assessed by a psychiatric facility."

I can still hear her voice. "We would never do that. That's not our policy!"

"I assure you, I asked the director to allow Mom to return to get the evaluation with the in-house psychiatric doctor. It was already scheduled. He was adamant that she could not return until she was assessed by a psychiatric facility. He even gave me the names of two facilities."

The financial manager had been reasonable and kind to Mom at the memory care, and I believed her. I was by Mom's side at the time of that conversation. I immediately left and went to the medical records department to retrieve a copy of the medical records from Mom's stay in the hospital psychiatric ward before she was sent to Ridgeview.

There it was in black and white: the memory care's statement of their reasons for not allowing Mom to be released back to the memory care.

> *"She needs to be cleared by Mental Health to return and also states that patient needs to be on medication to assist with aggressive behavior but family does not want her to have anything."*

It was *not* company policy. It was a staff member's strategy to override my authority with a doctor's order that would allow them to give her behavior medications. In my opinion, the memory care staff had an ulterior motive in sending Mom to the psychiatric facility. Their decision resulted in harm to her.

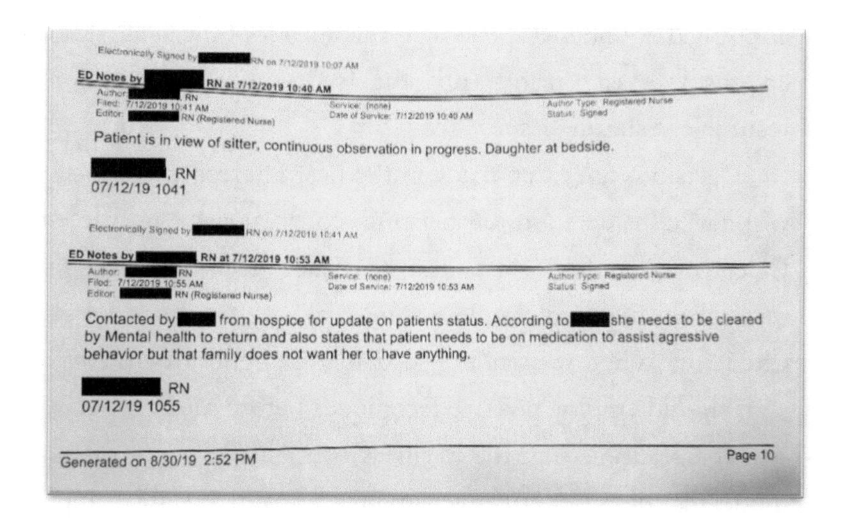

Electronically Signed by [redacted] RN on 7/12/2019 10:07 AM

ED Notes by [redacted] RN at 7/12/2019 10:40 AM

Author: [redacted], RN
Filed: 7/12/2019 10:41 AM
Editor: [redacted] RN (Registered Nurse)
Service: (none)
Date of Service: 7/12/2019 10:40 AM
Author Type: Registered Nurse
Status: Signed

Patient is in view of sitter, continuous observation in progress. Daughter at bedside.

[redacted], RN
07/12/19 1041

Electronically Signed by [redacted] RN on 7/12/2019 10:41 AM

ED Notes by [redacted] RN at 7/12/2019 10:53 AM

Author: [redacted] RN
Filed: 7/12/2019 10:55 AM
Editor: [redacted] RN (Registered Nurse)
Service: (none)
Date of Service: 7/12/2019 10:53 AM
Author Type: Registered Nurse
Status: Signed

Contacted by [redacted] from hospice for update on patients status. According to [redacted] she needs to be cleared by Mental health to return and also states that patient needs to be on medication to assist agressive behavior but that family does not want her to have anything.

[redacted], RN
07/12/19 1055

Generated on 8/30/19 2:52 PM — Page 10

This was a critical yet common crossroad and opportunity for caregiving to demonstrate an alternative approach to care. An opportunity to "Care for the person, fight the disease."

Were there alternative courses of action rather than sending Mom out for psychiatric evaluation and preventing her return? I think so. The staff could have adjusted to a more positive, soothing approach during toileting and showering. They could have tried a low dosage of Ativan and monitored her as I had agreed. They could have allowed the in-house psychiatric evaluation to determine the safest course of action for medication treatment.

Instead, the memory care sent her out of the facility and refused to let her return while they profited from a hefty, non-refundable recreational fee and two months' rent with one less resident to care for.

Memory care facilities should make every effort to keep residents in-house by partnering with psychiatric consultants, hospice in-patient facilities and other services to keep residents within safe, controlled boundaries. Sending residents out of the facility should be an absolute last resort, not the go-to approach to deal with insufficient staffing issues.

Decisions are often made in the best interest of the facility and without consideration of harmful consequences to the person. Caregivers, medical staff, and all other decision-makers should remember there are people behind LBD who want to be safe and cared for. When responding to dementia behaviors, memory care staff should employ positive techniques before medication.

The reality is that the business of memory care creates a care model that does not effectively train or encourage staff to apply such strategies. From a perspective of "We **Care** for the Person, We **Fight** the Disease," the PAC model, Teepa Snow's positive approach to care, offers an alternative approach to dealing with dementia behaviors. The facility staff was not interested in my attempts to suggest these techniques.

Another disappointment was that many memory care facilities don't know the effects of medication on LBD patients. Even in their profession, many of the nursing care staff assume the drugs work the same on all dementia patients. I was told, "We give it to all the patients that get aggressive."

The lesson I learned from this part of our journey was the most impactful. The typical or earlier versions of antipsychotics—first generation antipsychotics—can be *detrimental* to LBD patients. Research shows this. It is well documented. I found that information with minimal effort.

While first generation antipsychotic medications (e.g., Haloperidol) are commonly prescribed for Alzheimer's patients with behavioral challenges, these medications can negatively affect the brain of an individual with LBD, possibly causing severe side effects or even death.

For this reason, traditional antipsychotic medications like Haloperidol should be avoided. Some of the second generation or newer antipsychotic medications like Risperidone may also be problematic for someone with LBD. Seroquel, also referred to as Quetiapine, is preferred by some LBD experts. I found Seroquel in small doses to be the most effective for Mom in managing the sundowning and hallucinations. I only agreed to use the lowest-possible dose under careful observation for side effects. We used half of the lowest recommended dosage which was about 12.5mg per day. After Mom survived the cardiac arrest, I was more reluctant about leaving her side. I made sure any care facility knew not to give her any antipsychotics without my knowledge. When asked what she was allergic to, I gave the names of antipsychotics. I wrote on the board in her hospital room in large letters, "DO NOT GIVE ANTIPSYCHOTICS, CONTACT DAUGHTER!"

The Lewy Body Dementia Association (LBDA) published an article "Treatment of Behavioral Symptoms: When to Consider Antipsychotic Medications in LBD." It explains the difference between typical (first generation antipsychotics) and newer antipsychotics along with a list of antipsychotic medications. Below is an excerpt from the article:

> *In diseases such as schizophrenia, behavioral symptoms like hallucinations and delusions can be controlled using antipsychotic medications (also called neuroleptics). But in LBD, using antipsychotic medications can be problematic.*
>
> *We do not know why, but many people with LBD who are treated with antipsychotic medications have very severe reactions. Their cognitive symptoms can become worse and they may appear more sedated. In addition, they may have increased symptoms of parkinsonism. Also, in rare cases, antipsychotic medications may cause a condition called "neuroleptic malignant syndrome" (NMS), which causes severe fever, muscle rigidity and may lead to kidney failure and death. So, physicians must be very careful when prescribing antipsychotic medications for someone with LBD.*[2]

I have spoken with other family caregivers who question their decisions. If decisions are made out of love, there are no right or wrong decisions. When decisions are made out of love, the approach to care will lean toward a positive approach; when the decisions are made from a perspective of risk management, profit, and staffing issues medication is the default approach.

---

[2] "Treatment of Behavioral Symptoms: When to Consider Antipsychotic Medications in LBD," LBDA, accessed March 3, 2022, https://www.lbda.org/treatment-of-behavioral-symptoms-when-to-consider-antipsychotic-medications-in-lbd/

Chapter 6

HOSPITALS, DEMENTIA, AND ROLLERCOASTERS

Second Chance

After Mom went into cardiac arrest and was put on life support, she was in the ICU. We watched day by day to see if she would breathe on her own. It felt like slow motion. I'd gotten used to being by her side and didn't think much about what type of chair the room had or how much time I'd have to spend in it. The ICU chair wasn't very comfortable. Someone brought a second one so I could spread out a little as I worked in between the doctor and nurses coming into the room.

I had never seen Mom in this vulnerable state. Had Lewy caused this or the disappointing care systems? I had conversations with medical staff regarding the difficult decision of full code or resuscitation.

I had to give her a chance to live and laugh again.

The disease was difficult, but Mom was still there. If she could breathe on her own, she should have that opportunity.

She slowly woke up. Every day there was improvement until it was time to remove the breathing tube to see if she would breathe on her own.

She did. She became more alert and active. Eventually, she was moved to a regular recovery room. The hospital stays became the new whirlwind we were thrown into. Mom and I spent the next year in and out of hospitals.

LBD and Hospitals, *Oh My!*

Caring for a dementia patient in the hospital is an infinite loop. As long as Mom wasn't alert, she was an easy patient. As she got better and stronger, Lewy showed up and so would the Lewy behaviors. Imagine an LBD patient in a closed room with an IV in her arm, beeping noises, machines with lights, different people entering the room, some soft-spoken some loud, people poking and pricking you.

All of this created a scary situation for someone living with hallucinations in a foggy world. This was the perfect environment to incite agitation. The challenge was keeping her calm, especially at night if she didn't sleep. She might injure herself trying to get out of bed. Hospitals are not dementia-care facilities, so they don't have the time or patience to manage the dementia behaviors.

They're trying to provide medical care. During these times, it was a challenge to prevent hospital staff from giving her antipsychotics if she became agitated. Not all medical care professionals are aware of the potential harm of some medications on LBD.

No matter how small the rooms were, Aunt Betty and I took turns in those uncomfortable chairs, watching TV, nodding, and for me, working during the day. We seemed to keep her calm. After what she'd gone through, we didn't want another bad decision to cause a relapse. We wanted to protect her from another bad decision.

The hospital provided sitters to be sure Mom didn't harm herself at night. I learned this is considered a restraint. Physical restraints were sometimes used to prevent her from pulling the IV from her arm. I hated it but I understood.

Some care providers understood our concerns as her family. Those who understood and cared worked with Aunt Betty and me as members of the team. We helped them by being there to keep

Mom calm and safe. They offered us comfortable reclining chairs. We helped them do what they needed to do and focus on medical care.

At the same time, we made sure she wasn't given risky antipsychotics unless it was discussed and given in very low doses. Yes, we allowed behavior medication. We understood the need. We would have done the same thing with the memory care if they had worked with us collaboratively.

No Place for LBD

As Mom recovered from the cardiac arrest, it was apparent she wouldn't walk without assistance. She would need rehabilitation. Then began the infinite loop of finding a place for her to get care.

We had spent about six weeks in the hospital. The release process is another infinite loop. Most facilities would not accept unless she did not require restraints for three consecutive days. No night sitter and no physical restraints. We had to make sure she was safe, especially at night with no sitter.

The only way was for a family member to stay overnight. That was considered a visit, not a restraint/sitter. We counted each day we made it through without the restraints, or the count started over and a facility wouldn't accept her. In the meantime, the social worker would appear like the eviction police. I was given three days to find a place for her, or they would release her to the first place that had availability, regardless of how good or bad it was. So, I had to find a good place before they found a bad one.

Facilities I could afford and were decent wouldn't accept her because she had LBD. They only wanted people that wouldn't require a lot of care. The few places that accepted dementia patients, of course, had no space available. It was very difficult to get selected when a bed became available. I spent an exorbitant amount of time making phone calls, building relationships, and visiting the sites. I couldn't send her just anywhere, not this time.

As I tried to maneuver through the system of options for rehabilitation for Mom, I realized how uninformed and unavailable the industry was for LBD patients. Some facilities wouldn't consider taking her because she had LBD. Once, I was told, "We can't take 'them'. That's that 'bad dementia'. They can hurt you!"

Some wouldn't consider her because "agitation" was listed on her charts. Agitation is a very common behavior for dementia patients. Yet, memory care facilities that supposedly specialize in dementia care would only consider her if she didn't have aggressive behaviors. LBD patients were often labeled as aggressive and weren't considered for admission. There were insufficient care facility options for people like Mom with LBD.

The Ambulance Ride Gone Wrong

I continued vetting facilities that would provide rehab for Mom as she was prepared for release from the hospital. Through a contact, I found a nursing home that would admit her. They assured me the dementia behaviors were very familiar to their staff. Mom wouldn't stand out. Many of their residents had dementia.

The facility was close to my home and job. If she could regain the ability to walk, I would find good memory care where she could walk around again like she did at the memory care. I had a plan. After several long weeks, it was hospital-release day. Mom and I were eating lunch in her room at the hospital and waiting for the medical transport to take her to the nursing home rehabilitation facility. I snapped a picture with my cell phone.

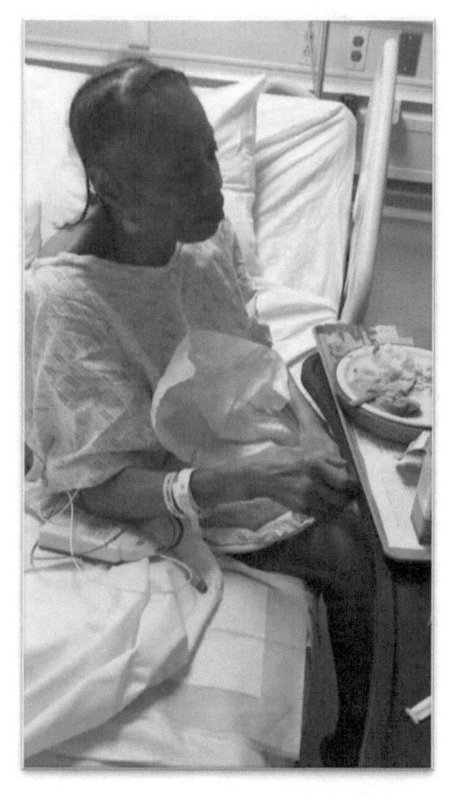

We talked and laughed as she sat on the side of her hospital bed and ate her lunch on her own. Two men finally arrived. One of the men asked me to sign for her to be transported. I signed then left to return a hospital tablet they'd given me during her stay to track her care.

I suppose I was gone too long. When I returned to the room intending to follow them out, the room was empty. They were gone! I rushed to my car and headed toward the nursing home so I could be there when the ambulance arrived. I knew this would be a new place for her, and after the psychiatric facility incident, I needed to manage this transition closely. I arrived and was told that she was in room 4A. I hurried to the room.

When I walked into the room, Mom was in the bed and no one else was in the room. I assumed someone would be with her since she had just arrived. She clearly wasn't the same as when we ate lunch together an hour before. She wasn't alert and wouldn't respond when I tried to wake her. I asked for a nurse to come to the room.

The nurses at the facility were nice ladies but showed no sense of urgency. This was her normal state to them. Three ladies came into the room as part of the normal intake process. I asked them what happened when she arrived. No one indicated that anything unusual had happened, and the ambulance transporters didn't communicate anything unusual either. I tried talking to Mom, but she wouldn't respond. My heart raced as I continued calling her name. When Mom responded, she couldn't talk to me. Only mumbling sounds came out as her eyes bulged wide and her arms extended out toward me. The nurse checked her BP. It was very low. I called the ambulance company. They said the notes indicated that Mom was combative during the transport, but they denied having given her anything to calm her.

We went through this a little while longer. I became more nervous but the nurses still weren't urgent. Finally, I opened my phone and showed the nurse the picture I'd just taken of Mom sitting on the hospital bed eating lunch a few hours ago. The nurse gasped. "Oh my God! *That's her*?"

"Yes, this was taken before the ambulance picked her up!"

"Now I see why you're so concerned! We thought this was her norm!" The unit nurse was attentive and continued monitoring her blood pressure. It was still very low and she wasn't responding.

"What do you want to do?" she asked. We had just left the hospital after being there for several weeks. Would I be overreacting to call this an emergency? I nervously decided to wait to see if her BP came back up. After another hour, the BP didn't increase and her state didn't improve. I decided to have Mom sent back to the hospital. That ambulance ride from the nursing home to Emory Hospital began my routine of always making sure I was there to talk directly to the ambulance drivers transporting my mom, appeal to their sense of compassion, and determine if I thought she was in good hands.

We arrived at Emory ER. I was there when the ambulance door opened. Mom was not alert. Ironically, the ER doctor that came in was one of my tennis teammates. After a few hours of monitoring and assessing in the ER room, the nurse seemed concerned. She said nothing, but I saw it on her face.

She briefly left the room and returned to explain that Mom was being moved to another room where they could monitor her BP more closely. They moved her to one of the rooms that had special emergency equipment. Mom's BP was dropping to dangerous levels, and they had to put her on different monitoring machines.

I sat outside the curtained room while several nurses, doctors, even my friend, all crowded the room. I sat there alone, wondering what happened from this morning—hospital release day—to now, being back in this familiar place of waiting, not knowing what would happen the next second.

My friend looked over at me from behind the curtain. She realized I was nervous and had no idea what was going on. She came over and explained that Mom's breathing was shallow and there were other complications. She had been intubated. I knew she'd been intubated after the cardiac arrest for several days. My first thought was, *she can't survive this again so soon. I'm going to lose her.*

This began another cycle of life support in the ICU. It was a nightmare. We couldn't get out of this hospital loop.

What happened during the ambulance ride from the hospital to the nursing home to cause this setback? We had lunch and I left the room. She was fine. The ambulance company said she was combative as they transported her from the hospital room.

I realized the scenario: Two Caucasian men approached her to take her. Depending on how they approached, or even the tone they used, may have been frightening for a black woman that grew up in the rural south. She couldn't understand what was happening. Did they address her by name? Did they talk to her calmly and assure her she was safe? Mom was frightened into a state of hysteria.

I'm not a scientific or medical expert. I'm a daughter and an advocate for my mom. From my perspective, anyone that encounters LBD patients should be trained on dementia behaviors and held accountable in applying that training in their professional interactions. Even ambulance drivers should understand the possible impacts of the transport process. Rolling on a narrow gurney in the air can feel unsafe and scary. It can cause agitation and even trauma. When she became combative, they should have paged me to return to the room; I was on the same floor.

A Better Ambulance Ride

While Mom was intubated in the ICU at Emory, the hospital pastor came by. He asked me, "Do you think it's her time?" I was calm and felt I was accepting our new state and the disappointment since she was sent out of the memory care.

I said, "If it is, then I accept it, but I don't think it's her time yet." It wasn't. Again, Mom woke up, but this time we saw more of the rallying. Mom would sleep for days, and no one could wake her. Hospice prepared me in case she didn't wake up. I was advised to consider feeding tubes and life support options.

Fortunately, she woke up. Aunt Betty and I took turns for four weeks in hospital room chairs at her bedside until she was cleared for release. The social worker, or hospital eviction police as I called her, started her release routine. We started the process of trying to get through three consecutive days without restraints. When release day came, I was right there.

The young EMTs who came to pick her up were personable and talked about their own grandmother. I explained her condition and what we experienced during the last ambulance transport. I was going to ride in the ambulance with her if I didn't feel comfortable. They assured me she was in good hands, so I followed behind.

The young man in the ambulance told me he played music for her during the transport. He played Sam Cooke and asked her if she liked it. She responded, "That was pretty good."

Chapter 7

THE NURSING HOMES

The Reality of Long-Term Care

The next few months began our experience with the good and bad of long-term care (LTC) facilities. Mom improved with rehab. I was hopeful she would walk again, even with the walker

LTC facilities have huge staffing issues. They can't watch residents all the time, and for LBD residents, safety is a concern. There are often several hours between each visual on the resident. Hours passed between changes for incontinent residents. Mom didn't know how to use the call button, and many times, no one responded anyway.

I was able to move Mom to the nursing home that I had selected when she was released from the hospital the first time. Mom's care needs and safety required more attention than what was provided by the nursing home staff. For these reasons, I hired personal caregivers who, along with Aunt Betty and I, provided most of the care for Mom in the nursing home. The hallways were wide, so she could move in her wheelchair. *If we can keep her hydrated, safe, clean, and dry, this will be better for her than home*, I thought.

Although nursing home staff are familiar with dementia, just like at the memory care center, sedation is the most common approach to care. Some of the staff knew how to approach her, but others didn't bother adjusting from one resident to the other.

The maintenance lady was kind and talked to her. Mom said, "That's my friend."

Mom got angry and uncooperative with some people. I observed the difference in their tone and how they approached her. It was obvious some staff just wanted to do what they needed to do and move on to the next resident.

No cameras were allowed in the LTC facility, so I visited around 7-8 AM to make sure she ate breakfast and was changed overnight. Sometimes I went back during lunchtime and then again after work.

The security guard noticed my frequent visits. "That must be a special lady because I know I've seen you here this morning already!"

Mom went through rehabilitation, and although I hoped she would walk again, I was told she couldn't walk safely on her own. She didn't have the stability and the dementia made it riskier. I was also told she probably couldn't learn to use the wheelchair as dementia patients don't learn new things.

I was afraid she'd be confined to the wheelchair sitting in one place. I was also concerned she'd try to walk because she didn't understand she couldn't walk, and that would be a safety risk. She quickly figured out she could move the chair with her feet, so she used her feet to walk in the chair. Before long, she was rolling around the hallways all over the nursing home. It was her version of walking, She was less confined. I was relieved of my worries when I visited Mom. Mom was confined to a wheelchair but she was able to talk and laugh with us. I called her sister, Lue, in South Georgia so she could talk to her family. Her voice was strong. "Hey, Lue, how is everybody doing? I love you."

During the day, Aunt Betty or the caregiver rolled her around so she could see other people and they sat outside in the sunshine with her. We bought snacks she liked and kept her hydrated with water or Pedialyte. We also kept her changed and dry if the staff couldn't do it. When she became agitated, we were there to redirect her and keep her safe. In the evenings, we helped her with her dinner plate and juice. Then we made sure she was clean and dry for bed. I often sat with her until she went to sleep. We realized the staff couldn't provide that level of care. There were a few who wanted to do more, but they were understaffed. Many didn't have the training to deal with the dementia behaviors.

"She's mean," one staff member told me. Some staff members didn't care and shouldn't have been employed in a nursing home.

My aunt had retired from a hospital. Hazel's granddaughter, the caregiver that worked with us at Clairemont, joined us again to help with Mom. She and Aunt Betty were well-trained on policies required by long-term care facilities to prevent bedsores, infection, falls etc. That led to conflicts between nursing home staff and the private caregivers because we were aware of the non-compliant activities.

The nursing home tried to find a policy that said private caregivers weren't allowed after allowing it for over four weeks. Whenever the facilities didn't like how we participated in care, they tried to find a way to get us out or go around us. My approach was always collaborative to find the best solution. I hoped that would be the facility's goal as well.

Pandemic Walkout Day

In March 2020, the nursing home received notice that facilities had to lock down and limit visitations. I was literally walked out of the nursing home because I stayed until I was told to leave or the police would be called. Nursing homes' responses to the emergency state created horrible experiences for many families. No one knew how bad it would get.

Families knew that care for their loved ones had decreased because the nursing homes were already understaffed. Families that provided care didn't know if their loved one would eat, get hydration, get diaper changes or lie in their own feces, get social stimulation, or feel safe. Aunt Betty, the private caregivers, and I had provided most of that care for Mom. Now, what would happen?

For many weeks, pandemic responses didn't include communication to families. I understood the care staff was busy, so I tried calling administration hoping someone would be designated to deal with family inquiries. There was no response. Some nurses allowed me to speak to Mom on the phone, others were obviously irritated by my calls.

I wrote letters requesting an exception to be made for those like my mom whose care was significantly impacted due to the absence of "essential caregivers". I proposed wearing personal protective equipment at my own expense, stating I would only go to a designated area with Mom. I tried to find a reasonable win-win solution.

I contacted the State Ombudsman Office, the nursing home corporate office, and wrote letters to senior advocate organizations. Window visits were established for allotted times, and I visited as often as allowed. When I observed through window visits that staff were not wearing masks, I made the unit nurse aware. The nurse yelled at me on the phone. "Well maybe they just took it off for a minute!" I observed another family member pleading to get information during a window visit. Things were frustrating on the floor, and they were taking it out on families trying to get information. There should have been a non-clinical person designated to communicate with families as the news about COVID outbreaks in nursing homes surfaced in the media.

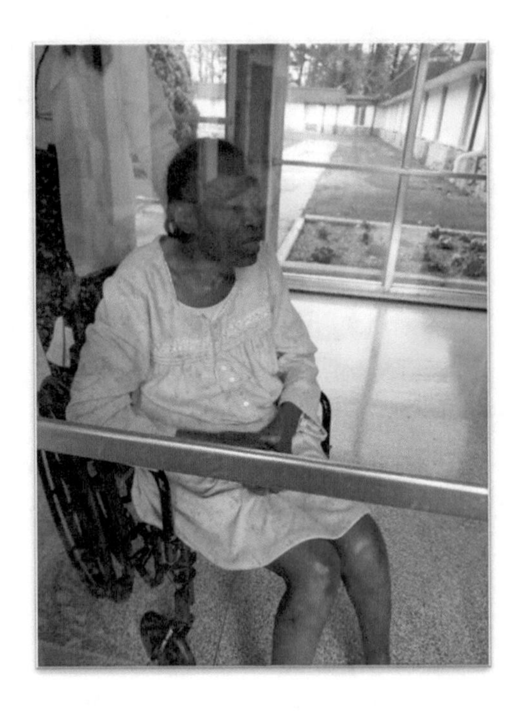

One Sunday morning, I was reading an updated status of COVID cases in nursing homes on the State Department of Public Health website. There were twenty-five additional cases in Mom's facility. No one had informed family there were *any* cases in the facility. When I called the state Ombudsman and the corporate office to get information, the nursing home staff interpreted it as complaints against them. I was only trying to get information on the risk status of the nursing home and the risks to my mom. The corporate office was responsive, but they called the nursing home to get a status on Mary Jackson, and I was labeled a "troublemaker". Below is an email I sent to one of the senior advocate organizations.

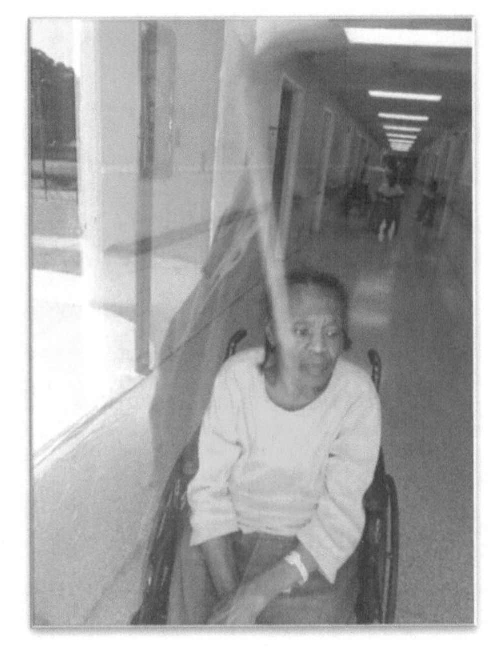

From: bmroache <█> Date: Friday, March 20, 2020

Subject: Nursing Home visitation restrictions without oversight To: HFRD.NH █████████

█████ *bmroache951@gmail.com*

I am a family member of a nursing home resident in the Atlanta community. Since the visitation restrictions were employed at local facilities, I am gravely concerned that the attention to the problems that plague many nursing homes have been given a legal right to put up a wall that could put residents in danger. I understand the need for the restrictions, no debate.

I am observing several things that the State HFRD should be aware of and concerned about. The rollout of restricted visitation is a huge change management program and should be implemented with **oversight, transparency, and communication.**

My primary concern is the ability for abuse and neglect to occur now that family is no longer allowed inside. Neglect and abuse have been a huge problem in nursing homes and the focus is not on this problem right now.

I beg the state to protect us all from COVID-19, I get it. But please require that these restrictions are implemented with **oversight** *from an outside entity that represents the residents and families, not the nursing homes. This is a critical part of the change management plan that is missing from the rollout of visitation restrictions.*

An **oversight pr***ogram should be employed IMMEDIATELY to ensure the safety of the residents and to ensure that regular communications are being provided to the family members that request it.* **Transparency** *should also be a key factor with the change rollout. For those family members requesting information, especially those who have medical power of attorney for residents lacking the capacity to speak for themselves, information should be available and regular.*

The restrictions employ a one-size-fits-all solution for every resident. Some facilities are not leveraging the "compassionate visitation" allowed by

CMS guidelines to minimize health risks for those residents whose health may decline as a result of no visitation.

Without the oversight of the state of Georgia, I have observed over the last two weeks, the nursing homes are employing restrictions at their discretion and families are having even window visitation rights taken away as a type of "punishment" for asking questions. When questions are asked, we are given very nebulous responses, not direct answers.

The Video Call with No Answer

The nursing home began video chats. I scheduled video chats and window visits as often as allowed. Sometimes, I did the video chat and the window visit on the same day. One day, Aunt Betty and I were ready as always for our twenty-minute opportunity to see and talk to Mom on a video chat.

When the camera was put on Mom, we saw she was distressed. She looked unresponsive, but that must have been common for most nursing home residents as no one noticed the difference. Because we had taken care of her, we had seen similar episodes. We knew if her blood pressure was too low, she could end up on life support again. My aunt and I called out to her.

"Sista! Sista! Mary Alice! Mary Alice!"

She couldn't respond. Her eyes were partially open. We knew she wasn't sleeping.

"Please get the nurse!"

The young lady administering the video chat asked for a nurse. A voice responded, "There's nothing wrong with her mother! She just sleeps like that!"

No one came to check on her. I knew this was in response to what the staff perceived as me overreacting. I called the unit desk to let them know Mom was in distress. I was told they would let the head nurse know when she returned. There was no sense of urgency.

I jumped in my car and drove to the nursing home. No one answered my calls at the desk. My mind was racing and I couldn't let her sit there and decline. I had to get help for her. I couldn't go inside, so I tried to see her from the window of her room, but I couldn't see anything. Desperate to get some attention to her or at least make sure she wasn't in need of immediate help, I called the corporate office from the parking lot. I informed them of the urgent situation and that I was unable to confirm that my mother received any attention.

Finally, the unit nurse on the wing went to Mom's room. She called me back and acknowledged that Mom's state wasn't typical and her BP was low. I could tell by her tone that she was nervous about the situation. She realized the staff had ignored the situation for forty-five minutes on her watch. She attempted to defend the failure to respond sooner. I didn't want to hear it at the time, I just wanted her to help my mom. I was still outside in the parking lot. They decided to send Mom to the hospital. I waited outside to lay my eyes on Mom when the ambulance brought her out of the nursing home. I told her I was there and that I loved her. The ambulance drivers assured me they would take good care of her.

I was familiar with Emory Hospital now. I was allowed into the ER room to see her. When I walked in, a COVID test was being administered. During the night, several tests were ordered. I sat in the chair by her bedside nodding off and on. Her vitals were better and the COVID test came back negative. They admitted her into the hospital, and I said goodbye. I couldn't go to the floor due to COVID restrictions.

While Mom was in the hospital, I received more communication, compassion, and understanding from the hospital staff than I had received from the nursing home staff. I understood everyone's job was made difficult with the pandemic.

Several nurses made sure they got a phone to Mom's ear so she could hear my voice. It was done with an attitude of compassion and understanding of the family's role in the care spectrum. Once, the nurse at Emory used her personal cell phone when the landline wouldn't reach the bed. She said they couldn't get Mom to talk. When she put the phone to Mom's ear to hear my voice, Mom said, "Hey Bonnie, I'm doing all right." The nurse couldn't understand her, but I did.

"I'm amazed Mary's smiling. We haven't seen her respond like that." The hospital staff volunteered information and let me know what was going on with her condition, unlike the nursing home.

As she stabilized, I began calling facilities to see if I could have her transferred to another nursing home. No one was willing to take a new patient, especially with staff shortages. It was too risky. After a few days, she was stable enough to be released back to the same nursing home.

Nursing homes and all LTC facilities can and must do better in emergency situations. Communication is a key component of an emergency response plan. Just as there were frequent communications with public health officials, there should have been regular communications with family.

Shortly after I contacted corporate, families began receiving weekly updates on the COVID status of the facility.

The staff saw me as demanding and controlling. Perhaps I rubbed some of them the wrong way. As I reflect on those events and my collaborative personality style, I know I was always respectful, appreciative, and only interested in making sure my mom was cared for and safe. If there was any conflict, it was because our goals weren't aligned.

A Better Place for Mom

In June 2020, I was able to accompany Mom to a medical appointment at the Hyperbaric Center at Emory. I was glad to be able to spend time with her. The medical transporter was kind to her. Mom talked to him during the drive and he talked to her like she was his mother. It was amazing how some healthcare professionals understood how to interact with her while others shouldn't have been in the field of personal care.

That appointment in June was the last time I would spend quality time with her. There was a mix-up on our pickup time, so we had a long wait for the transport after the appointment. We waited in the Emory Midtown Hospital downstairs lobby; the same lobby we were in four years earlier when I watched her sitting on the bench and realized how vulnerable she was.

Now, in the same lobby, she was in a wheelchair. She rolled around in the mostly-empty hallway. She knew who I was. I ordered food in the cafeteria when I realized she wouldn't be back at the nursing home in time for dinner. I observed that she could still pick up her own food and feed herself. She ate chicken fingers and reached for the cup of water and drank it on her own.

I had an apple and asked if she wanted some. She responded, "Yes, I'll take some." I was glad to see she was still able to respond, eat, and drink with minimal help. That meant she could still do well in a memory care facility. I just needed to find a good place. I needed to get her out of that nursing home and into an environment where she could move around in the wheelchair and safely communicate with people around her.

In June, I focused on finding a memory care facility. It was even more challenging because of the pandemic. Facilities were more short-staffed than before and most weren't accepting new residents. Mom had been tested for COVID eight or nine times between the nursing home and two hospital visits. All tests were negative, thank God.

Two facilities accepted her after an on-site assessment. I selected a memory care facility. I talked to the nursing director, facility director, and other staff. They not only allowed cameras, they encouraged and offered them. That was a first.

They also installed a plexiglass screen to support visual visits by family. The move date was set for July 1, 2020. On June 30, the day before moving to the new memory care, I received a call from the nursing home. I was informed that Mom had fallen out of her chair but was ok and in bed. Tests were being ordered to check for damage. I would realize later how bad that fall really was.

We moved her the next day as planned. When I saw her during the move, she seemed fine but not talkative. Within the next few days, bruises under her eye and a knot on the middle of her forehead began to form. The scan of her head showed no damage.

The new memory care facility seemed like a good fit for her needs. There were hallways to roll about We did regular virtual visits using Zoom. Some of the nurses actually read Mom's history and called her by her nickname, "Sista", to make her feel comfortable.

Mom began trying to get out of the wheelchair and that began the impasse of restraints. By law, the facility couldn't restrain residents to keep them safe. It would violate their rights. People have a right to fall. In my opinion, the laws don't consider that someone with dementia cannot express their right to be restrained or to fall.

The facility couldn't accept my permission as her medical POA to allow restraints to keep her safe. In essence, that law is designed to protect resident rights, however, it prevents the use of these devices to protect their body.

Per my research, facilities *can* utilize restraints if it's helpful to the resident and a doctor has written an order so it's included in the care plan. Instead, I was often told the law prevents the use of restraints altogether.

I understand the reason for the law. However, I think the interpretation is an example of "throwing the baby out with the bathwater."

This place was a bit farther away from me, but I watched her on the camera in the evenings. I still visited her from the window often.

Mom never regained the level of alertness she had the day she was sent out of the memory care facility in July 2019. She wasn't as alert as a few weeks prior when I accompanied her to the hyperbaric doctor appointment at Emory.

She continued declining and was at the memory care only about three weeks when she started having seizure-like episodes. Again, she was sent to the hospital. It was mid-July 2020. The pandemic was fully impacting hospitals and other facilities.

I always made sure I was there when the ambulance arrived so I could lay eyes on her and tell her I was there before they took her inside. I sat in the hospital ER, as safely as possible, six-feet apart from others, waiting to hear how she was. This was a familiar place for me, but it was still unnerving. You never get used to that quiet room they take you to in the ER to hear the news.

The nurse came to the quiet room, and I was told Mom was not responding but was stable. After about two to three days, she must have come out of it. The nurse reported that she was talking and trying to get out of bed. *That's good. That's her normal behavior*, I thought. I hoped she would be back at the memory care soon rolling around in her wheelchair.

The hospital inquired several times about the knot on her head. They ran tests and didn't find any damage. This was consistent with the test results reported by the nursing home after the fall occurred. They never found exactly what incited the seizure episodes.

After a few more days in the hospital, Mom was alert enough to take the swallow test so she could eat and be released. Instead, she slipped back into sleeping a lot and wasn't awake enough to pass the swallow test. The hospital contacted me every day with an update. Every day she was sleeping and a swallow test couldn't be done.

Four days into this unresponsive state, the hospital asked me to come to visit her. I realized later they wanted me to see her for myself. They felt there was nothing more they could do.

Hospice talked to me about decisions I needed to make. I had been in this familiar place before. Mom always woke up and started eating and drinking liquids.

This time felt different.

The impact of that decision to send her for a psychiatric evaluation had taken its toll over the last twelve months.

Chapter 8

THE FINAL JOURNEY

The Roller Coaster Ride Slows Down

In late July 2020, I went to WellStar Hospital in Marietta as I had many times after the cardiac arrest incident in July a year earlier. Due to the pandemic, the hospital was different. After going through check-in to confirm I'd been given an exception to visit, I entered the room where Mom was sleeping. She lay there with the vital machines connected. She just needed to be alert so they could feed her by mouth, and she could be released.

I cautiously put a drop of water on her bottom lip to see if she would respond. She did. She took a few drops of water. I knew the risks. I talked to her and told her I was there. She responded faintly, "I know."

Mom squeezed my hand. I knew she was still there, and she knew I was there. They let me visit every day for the next three days, but she didn't wake up.

This time it was different.

I made the difficult call for final arrangements. I wrote out the obituary and made sure all the pictures I would need were accessible. Then I faced reality and I cried.

I had watched her come back from those sleep episodes to sharing memories, talking, laughing, and eating meals with us many times. She was fighting. I had to give her every opportunity to live if it didn't cause her more suffering.

We agreed to move her to hospice and provide total parenteral nutrition (TPN) through IV to see if she would respond positively. If not, I didn't want to apply the feeding tube to her tired body.

Mom still wasn't alert. It had been about seven days without nutrition. I came home to complete the workday and would return in the evening. The hospice called a few hours later. Those phone calls always caused anxiety. The nurse said, "Ms. Roache, I want to inform you that we didn't administer the nutrition to your mom." Before I could ask what happened, she said, "Your mom is awake."

"*Really?*"

"And she is eating on her own."

"WHAT?" I could not believe it.

"She's eating yogurt and she drank a cup of juice." I was elated!

I wanted to bring her home. We were working from home due to the pandemic and we had already started the process of moving from our townhouse to a house with space for her. As soon as that was ready, we would move her home.

Something changed. Mom was awake but much calmer. The effects of the fall from her last night in the nursing home were evident as she had a large hematoma in the middle of her forehead. It had been tested twice for damage with negative results. The hematoma would last for several weeks.

She stabilized and I sat next to her many days working on my computer as she slept in hospice. The dementia behaviors were different. She wasn't agitated, and she didn't fight when the staff changed her. Maybe she was too tired.

The Ride on I-285

After about two weeks, hospice called and informed me that Mom was stable and needed to be released. The memory care agreed that she could return temporarily until I set up space in the townhouse to bring her home. I needed a few weeks to do that. She was released back to memory care around August 5, 2020.

As I followed the ambulance from McDonough to Smyrna on I-285, the memory care director and a corporate nurse called my cellphone. They discussed their concern about Mom's care at the facility. I didn't quite comprehend at the time what they were really saying. The ambulance arrived at the memory care. I parked my car and sat to focus on what they were saying.

I realized they were telling me they wouldn't take her back. The ambulance sat just outside the front door of the memory care with Mom inside on a hot August day. A corporate decision had been made that overturned the memory care's decision. I had continued to pay the monthly rent. I didn't have another place for her to go and my house space wasn't ready yet. It seemed so heartless at the time. How could they evict her from memory care?

This felt like when she wasn't allowed to return to the first memory care until she had the psychiatric evaluation. The hospice facility and ambulance drivers were all in shock. The ambulance, with Mom inside, headed back to I-285 and returned Mom to the hospice facility.

I needed to prepare that space to bring my mom home. My husband and I spent the next few days doing just that. I remember that weekend well. The day the hospice nurse informed me that Mom was awake and wouldn't need the TPN was the day I learned that her dear sister Johnnie had passed. I missed Aunt Johnnie's homegoing service on August 7 because I had to get the space ready to bring Mom home.

It wasn't until later that I felt grateful the memory care didn't take her back.

After that incident, I understood that memory care facilities are businesses first. Decisions are made based on risks, liabilities, and profit. The facility management were decent people, and the decision to not allow her back that day was likely out of their hands. I actually believe the director of both memory care facilities I'd dealt with were decent people and wanted to do the right thing. I prayed for them both.

Mom's Gift to Me

Mom came home to our townhouse in August 2020. The new house would be ready in a few months and there was a room for Mom. Hospice advised me to keep her comfortable and not feed her due to risks of asphyxiation. I was given a box of medications called the Emergency Kit.

I reached out to the caregiver we'd called Cousin Hazel's granddaughter. She had taken good care of Mom in Clairemont and the nursing homes. I trusted her. She demonstrated what a good caregiver should be. Once again, she joined our team to help care for Mom while I worked upstairs.

I wanted Mom to feel safe since she had been moved to various facilities and hospitals over the last year. "You're home! You're home with your family!" I wasn't sure if she could hear me. She wasn't speaking or active at first but she was awake. "I'm your daughter. I'm Bonnie! I'm here!"

I was trying to say things that would make her feel comfortable and safe. Suddenly, she said very clearly, "I know that, and that's a good thing." Mom never ceased to surprise me. That was a good thing indeed.

Mom was confined to the bed, but she could sit up and talk. Although I understood the risks of asphyxiation, I carefully started feeding her. She ate and regained strength, allowing her to pick up her own food. She insisted on holding her own cup. We made sure she stayed dry and clean and comfortable. She and Hazel's granddaughter had more conversations about those ol' folks like they used to at Clairemont. Aunt Betty visited often as well.

One day, I was helping her eat, and I gave her a cup of water. She took it and as I turned away, I heard her say, "Thank you." She reached out, took my hand, and pulled it to her mouth. She kissed the back of my hand and said, "I Love You."

I was amazed and filled with a sense of peace. It was the gift I needed to know that she was finally in a good place. On that day, I wasn't sure if she knew I was her daughter or that I was Bonnie, but she knew I was someone she loved. It confirmed for me again that, although LBD had stolen so much, it had not taken away her ability to feel loved and to express love to me. That was the greatest gift of all. We enjoyed more time talking and laughing. I was still experiencing and learning on this journey.

Maya Angelou said, "People may forget what you said, but they will never forget how you made them feel." I believe the same thing holds true with someone with LBD and other brain-altering diseases. They may not remember who you are, but can feel loved and safe.

This is a critical and simple philosophy for caregivers and anyone interacting with LBD patients.

In August, the LBDA contacted me to ask if I would share our journey to help raise awareness and financial support. The story was published on the LBDA site in November 2020, titled "*A Daughters Love*" and "*The Bond That Lewy Could Not Break*."[3]

Our Journey Ends

On December 6, 2020, Mom turned eighty-three. Shortly afterward, she was alert but stopped swallowing. She held food in her mouth, sometimes for a long time. I think she forgot how to swallow. After a few days without eating, she slept more and more.

When she was awake, we talked. She said the names of her brothers, Donnell and Earnest. I couldn't understand everything, but I understood the names. They both had transitioned years earlier. One day, she called out the name, "Johnnie!"

I asked, "Do you see Johnnie?"

She faintly responded, "Yes." I noticed the metamorphosis occurring in her face. That hematoma from the fall in the nursing home had disappeared. Her complexion became even toned and clear. I stared at her.

"Mom, you are beautiful." I talked to her about the good place she was going to. "All those people will be so glad to see you coming. You all are going to have such a good time!" Tears flowed but I had a sense of peace.

On January 5, 2021, Mom passed peacefully at home. Our journey had ended.

---

[3] "A Bond that Lewy Couldn't Break," LBDA, November 2020, https://www.lbda.org/give2020/?mkt_tok=NjIyLUxNRS03MTgAAAAAYVax8IwqLIZVtbRhWvTRSBdAuvQeFuFAnG6c5odTKTHe813J-OVEjC6czHiW

The new house with a room for her was ready a month later.

In honor of Mother's Day, the LBDA published a follow-up story to continue awareness and support titled "*Our Journey Comes to an End.*"[4]

I Pray for a Better Care Experience Tomorrow

I pray that all facilities, private or state-funded, will not only allow cameras, but have them become a standard part of the room setup. Families should be allowed access to view cameras from their computers and smartphones. I understand privacy concerns, but this deserves strategic thinking because the benefits far outweigh the risks.

I pray that some restraints will be allowed when it makes sense. A sitter for a Lewy body dementia patient in a hospital should not be considered a restraint for the purpose of long-term care admission.

I pray that the caregiver industry will require highly skilled resources and compensation will be commensurate with the level of skill and performance. The performance should include the application of positive approaches to care along with pharmaceutical approaches to care when possible.

I pray that families will always be considered part of the care team for their loved ones.

I pray that all facilities and professional caregiver certification programs will provide training on positive techniques such as the PAC model by Teepa Snow. I pray caregivers will be held

---

[4] "Mary Alice Jackson, Our Journey Comes To An End," LBDA, May 2021, https://www.lbda.org/lbda_story/our-journey-comes-to-an-end/?fbclid=IwAR1DQ25GFOz0eCnVM5BnqG2gzxCNg7j_kv-c4QdZXVEJdthnvdkSTnG5m38

accountable and encouraged to employ these techniques to address dementia behaviors.

The pandemic has taught many lessons about the value of essential caregiver visits. Isolation kills, too. Just talk to any of the thousands of families in the state of New York who lost loved ones in nursing homes in 2020. Their stores are heartbreaking and I pray for them.

I pray for a cure to this unrelenting disease.

Mary Alice concentrates on her work

Appendix

Strategies to Care for LBD patients. *Some of these are directly from the Dementia Care Specialist Resource and some of these are based on our personal journey.*

- Don't approach from the back. They can't see you.
- Keep an even voice tone.
- Use short specific sentences when requesting.
- Smile, make them feel safe.
- Don't get too close in their face. It may frighten them.
- Try to manage them one on one with others nearby to help if needed. Try not to have three or more people approach at the same time.
- Anyone that comes in contact with LBD (dementia) persons—whether you're direct care, food services, maintenance, ambulance drivers, non-emergency transport, etc.—should know how to apply these simple strategies.
- Play soft music in the background or their favorite music genre.

List of Helpful Tools and Aids:

- Smartsole Shoe Tracking Device: www.smartsole.com
- Tile brand tracker
- Auto-shut off electric kettle
- Manual turn microwave dial
- Water leak detector
- Amcrest Pro Security Camera
- Automatic pill dispenser with flashing light reminder and locking pill compartments to only allow access to the pills to be taken
- Little plastic containers at Dollar Tree – can be used for pill boxes

Educational Resources Referenced:

- Dealing With Dementia: A Caregiver's Guide by Rosalynn Carter Institute For Caregiving
- The Caregiver's Support Kit. National Caregiving Foundation

- Medicaid CCSP Community Care Service Program – waiver to help pay for caregiver services to keep your loved one home and out of facilities
- Atlanta Regional Commission BRI Program – wealth of resources
- Where The Heart Is Senior Placement Service – Eddie Biggers cares and tries to find the right place
- Teepa Snow, Positive Approach to Care – provides alternative methods to dementia care. Reference Positive Approach To Care at www.teepasnow.com
- Emory Integrated Memory Care Center – Brain Health Center Services a primary care physicians dedicated for the treatment of dementia patients

Antipsychotic Medications

There are two types of antipsychotic medications: the typical (or traditional) antipsychotics and the newer, antipsychotics.

The typical antipsychotics were the first antipsychotics developed and should NOT be prescribed for people with LBD. Typical antipsychotics include:

- chlorpromazine (Thorazine)
- droperidol (Inapsine)
- fluphenazine (generic only)
- haloperidol (Haldol)
- loxapine (Loxitane)
- molindone (Moban)
- perphenazine (generic only)
- pimozide (Orap)
- thioridazine (generic only)
- thiothixene (Navane)
- trifluoperazine (Stelazine)

The newer or **atypical** antipsychotics may be helpful for people with LBD if used conservatively. Atypical antipsychotics include:

- aripiprazole (Abilify)
- clozapine (Clozaril)
- fluoxetine & olanzapine (Symbyax)

- iloperidone (Fanapt)
- olanzapine (Zyprexa)
- paliperidone (Invega)
- quetiapine (Seroquel)
- risperidone (Risperdal)
- ziprasidone (Geodon) [5]

[5] "Treatment of Behavioral Symptoms," LBDA, accessed March 3, 2022, https://www.lbda.org/treatment-of-behavioral-symptoms-when-to-consider-antipsychotic-medications-in-lbd/

Acknowledgments

A special thanks to Aunt Betty. You showed up when I expected, when I didn't expect it, when you didn't feel like it, and when I needed you. You were Mom's first daughter.

A special thanks to Laronda Jones, a.k.a. Hazel's granddaughter. Laronda, you were the epitome of what a caregiver should be. You were knowledgeable in your craft, you were dependable, and you cared. You provided what family members need in a caregiver: the ability to breathe for a while knowing your loved one is with someone who cares.

A sincere thank you to my cousin, Donna Sheree Stewart. Your expertise as a nurse and hospice professional helped me to communicate with medical staff and understand my options to make informed decisions.

Thank you to Willette Mosby-Reynolds for your expertise and time to read and edit my first draft.

The Lewy Body Dementia Association and Teepa Snow Positive Approach to Care for providing a platform to share our journey.

The Cecil Pittman Foundation

Peace Baptist Church Dementia Support Group

The Branches Class of Greenforest Community Baptist Church who allowed Mom to join our fulfillment hour class.

The Atlanta Regional Commission BRI program.

I want to thank those who showed up in various ways when we needed you. Those who sat with her when I asked or provided a listening ear, Yvette Cummings, Mary Austin, and Mitzi Higgins in particular. Those who called, sent texts or emails to check on us, sent flowers and cards when she was in the hospital, provided flexibility to work my job remotely and those who were kind to her and saw beyond the disease.

Finally, thank you Steven L Roache Sr. for your support and patience during my absence physically and emotionally.

Made in the USA
Columbia, SC
21 March 2024